THE GREENEST BUILDING: How the Bullitt Center Changes the Urban Landscape

An Ecotone Publishing Book/2016
Copyright © 2016 by Mary Adam Thomas

Ecotone Publishing — an Imprint of the International Living Future Institute

For more information write:

Ecotone Publishing
721 NW Ninth Avenue, Suite 195
Portland, OR 97209

Author: Mary Adam Thomas
Book Design: softfirm
Edited by: Fred McLennan

Library of Congress Control Number: 2015951067
Library of Congress Cataloging-in Publication Data

ISBN 978-0-9827749-6-0

1. ARCHITECTURE   2. ENVIRONMENT   3. PHILOSOPHY

First Edition

Printed in Canada on FSC-certified paper, processed Chlorine-Free, using vegetable-based inks.

THE GREENEST BUILDING

How the Bullitt Center
Changes the Urban Landscape

LIVING
BUILDING
CHALLENGE

TABLE OF CONTENTS

Photo: Nic Lehoux

FOREWORD: BULLITT PROOF

The Bullitt Center needs no help here trumpeting numbers. Bullitt proves we can design and produce a high performing commercial office building that yields social and mechanical superlatives in every category of environmental ethics: energy saved, rainwater collected, waste reused, codes rewritten, communities formed, and cities advised. The design of the Bullitt Center blends novel building systems with novel social systems, using material architecture to structure choice architecture. This book tells that data-rich story in great detail. I have a slightly different question for the reader: How does the building perform visually, as a composition?; also, how does it perform spatially, as a modern social and urban artifact?

Responsible architectural historians and critics don't judge buildings in a vacuum, based on fashion or taste. Their standards for urban and architectural composition derive from noble criteria first articulated by Leon Battista Alberti, a fifteenth century lawyer, priest, urbanist, and architect of the Renaissance Ideal City. Alberti's most famous analogy still applies today: "The city is like some large house, and the house... in turn like some small city." This sentence appears in book one, chapter nine of his treatise, On the Art of Building, which Alberti wrote in part to update and improve the first architectural treatise written in the West, by the Roman architect Marcus Vitruvius Pollio, 27 BCE. Of course, the Bullitt Center is not a house; typologically, it's a workplace. Bullitt nevertheless expressly positions itself and its tenant community as an analogy for the whole city, which is appropriate, since the words most relevant to its program, "economy" and "ecology," derive from the Greek root oikos, "household"—respectively, "household management," and "the study of the household of nature."[1]

Alberti based his rigorous compositional standards for the design and composition of buildings and cities on the codes of antiquity, in particular harmonic Pythagorean ratios and Euclidean geometric forms. Alberti's standards were less concerned with aesthetic enrichment than political stability. The signature of the Ideal City was nature itself, in particular its most "perfect" manifestation, the human body, whose abstracted proportions constituted the lines and angles of an extramundane geometric order. By his house-

1 *Oxford English Dictionary*, s.v. "economy" and "ecology," www.oed.com.eres.library.manoa.hawaii.edu (accessed Ocrober 1, 2015)

city analogy, Alberti sought to extend the ideals of domestic virtue across the whole fabric of urban life. His ideal city aimed to mitigate the threat of ill fortune and human folly through its compositional virtue. By virtue, Alberti means "excellence" and "good action," as the theorist Joseph Rykwert notes, free from any "moral patina," rather a kind of "gifted activism in matters pertaining to civic life and society."[2]

This is where the Bullitt Center and Alberti converge. In Alberti's house-city analogy, beauty is not a superfluous visual or sensual pleasure, but rather a platform for productive political relations, for a healthy body politic. The material and ethical disposition of the city are one and the same problem. In other words, ornament and rhetoric are not surplus to the city—and not subservient to "building performance"; they are its essential, constitutive ingredients, the source of both spatial and political efficacy. In a word, people behave better in physically beautiful environments. Bullitt bets that people will behave better in high-performing

environments, moreover, that "beauty" is embodied in performance as much or more than appearance. This has always been the case in dance, athletics, theater, and music.

Alberti sees virtue as the civil corollary of beauty, derived from the Greek idealization of the human form—"that reasoned harmony of all the parts within a body, so that nothing may be added, taken away, or altered but for the worse." Nowadays most contemporary architects eschew this principle, leading to increasingly esoteric and self-referential building forms, either banal or provocative, often both at the same time. Notwithstanding, the underlying principle of the unity of relation between part and whole remains a vital question, especially if we accept the interdependency of natural and human systems. However you define it, "good form" is always first and foremost suitable to its context.

Bullitt's roof alone suggests the need to rethink what it is we're talking about when we talk about the relation between part and whole. Its roof is the first thing everybody notices about the building. It sets it apart from all other buildings in the region; and it marks the building iconographically, both in the neighborhood and the city. Of course, the form

2   Joseph Rykwert and Robert Tavernor, "Glossary," in Leon Battista Alberti, *On the Art of Building in Ten Books*, ed. and trans. J. Rykwert and R.Tavernor (Cambridge: MIT Press, 1988), 421–22.

of the roof is strictly performance-driven: it's a flat solar hat of photovoltaic cells that serves as a key ingredient in the building's realization of verifiable net zero energy. The architects correctly relieve its ungainly size and proportion by perforating the plane with a pattern of openings in the photovoltaic grid, letting daylight through and framing patches of Seattle's infamously grey sky when seen from the street.

The Bullitt Center goes a long way to reconcile the exigencies of design with the exigencies of environmental integrity embodied in Living Building standards, which it handily meets or exceeds, the first Class A office building in history to do so. The design team's problem was how to shape the building to house not only people, but data. Data is the medium through which the client, Denis Hayes, communicated his unyielding performance goals. People and their behavior—using the "irresistible stair," showering at work, monitoring their electrical outlets, and agreeing to leases that aim to idle not just elevators but also cars—these are choices and requirements of occupancy that fuel the Bullitt Center's Living Building Challenge-compliant data. Occupants will have more reasons to feel healthy and happy beside a sexy stairway and a comfortable place to shower:

they'll have tall ceilings, commodious volume, abundant light, fresh air, breathtaking views, simple circulation, richly-hued exposed wood structure, natural finishes, and generous amenities such as well-equipped community kitchens.

The Bullitt Center houses data and people that never lose sight of global warming and climate change. Form emerges as much or more from its ethical context as its urban context. Performance, not appearance, embodies its ethical compass. The Bullitt Center excels in its demonstration of the kind of knowledge that produces meanings faithful to principles of utility, not grace. Form (as Rob Peña declares in his excellent case study) follows performance.

My question here has to do with everything that is surplus to utility. Lewis Hyde describes this surplus value as a kind of "gift property" that "serves an upward force," which provides a suitable annotation for all great architecture.[3] Unfortunately, 95 percent of all commercial buildings in the world trivialize architectural principle, but not a single molecule of the

3 Lewis Hyde, *The Gift: Imagination and the Erotic Life of Property* (New York: Vintage Books, 1979), 25.

Bullitt Center is trivial. Few, if any, office buildings expressly aimed at a public audience go as far as the Bullitt Center in seeking to balance good looks with good guts, but the guts are where the news is; consequently, you will find Bullitt's real beauty under its skin, in its elegant mechanical organs.

Elaine Scarry describes beauty's effect as an "unceasing begetting." In great philosophy and literature, she observes, beauty "sponsors… the idea of eternity, the perpetual duplicating of a moment that never stops. But it also sponsors the idea of terrestrial plenitude and distribution, the will to make 'more and more' so that there will eventually be 'enough.'"[4] The mitigation of global climate change reverses this logic. We need to make less and less so that there will eventually be enough; or, conversely, we need to make more and more that consumes less and less so that there will eventually be enough. In this sense, Bullitt unceasingly begets attention to conscience and posterity.

The Bullitt Center expresses the potential of architecture to show us what data-driven building form really looks like and how it changes our criteria for success. The building demonstrates how architecture can better engage and collaborate with more privileged branches of knowledge that command empirical data—environmental systems, civil and mechanical engineering, and urban ecology. It shows us how architecture can visually magnetize the public imagination by authentically engaging "grand challenge" problems through systems that measure impact on energy, climate, the environment, urbanization, information, health, and social equity. In its deft, diagrammatic formalism and its effective integration of science and data within its very bones, The Bullitt Center satisfies Stan Allen's criteria for "difference that makes a difference."[5] For proof, just look at the roof.

DANIEL S. FRIEDMAN

5

4   Elaine Scarry, "On Beauty and the Just," The Tanner Lectures on Human Values (Yale University, March 25 and 26, 1998), 5.

5   Stan Allen, *Practice: Architecture, Technique + Representation* (New York: Routledge, 2009), xvi–xviii.

ACKNOWLEDGEMENTS

This book, much like the building it celebrates, exists because of the efforts of a much longer list of people than those who are popularly recognized for their contributions. As I express my gratitude to the key players, I also give a nod to all who toil behind the scenes to support and enhance the work of the visionaries mentioned in these pages. Thank you for your dedication—to your firm, your non-profit, your community, and the environmental movement at large. You are valuable agents of change.

As for the aforementioned key players, many people generously carved time out of their very busy schedules to share with me the details of how the Bullitt Center came to be. I could not have pieced together this jigsaw puzzle without them. Whether or not they are quoted directly in the chapters that follow, these individuals (listed alphabetically) helped round out the story: Wendy Abeel, Scott Bevan, Conrad Brown, Marc Brune, Mark Buehrer, Harriet Bullitt, Brian Court, Joe David, Steve Doub, Chris Faul, Marisa Hagney, Jim Hanford, Deb Hartl, Denis Hayes, Morgan Hudson, Brad Kahn, Rachael Meyer, Jonathan Morley, Colleen Walsh Neely, Christian LaRocco, Rob Peña, Brett Phillips, Russ Porter, Doug Raff, Corey Reilly, Byron Richards, McKenzie Richardson, Ron Rochon, Chris Rogers, Casey Schuchart, George Schuchart, Paul Schwer, Margaret Sprug, Justin Stenkamp, Steven Strong, Diane Sugimura, Bonnie Tabb, and Maggie Walker. Thank you for accommodating my demands on your time and attention.

When Jason F. McLennan asked me to take on this assignment, I was humbled by his confidence in me. Thank you, Jason, for allowing me to write about a project that is so near and dear to you—and that so powerfully represents your vision for a Living Future.

Michael Berrisford somehow manages to do virtually everything at Ecotone Publishing, yet always makes time for my calls. Mike, you are a pleasure to work with and for. Thanks to Erin Gehle and Johanna Björk for waving their magic design wand once again and turning my black-and-white Word document into a colorful thing of beauty. I am also grateful to Fred McLennan for his keen editing eye.

Although I write in silence and solitude, I cogitate noisily and publicly. I deeply appreciate my friends and family who listened to me talk about, wrestle with, and fixate on this project for many months. Thank you for hearing me out. To my dinner table companions—Kevin, Mackenzie, and Reed—you are my favorite sounding boards.

MARY ADAM THOMAS

AUTHOR PROFILE

MARY ADAM THOMAS

Mary Adam Thomas is an independent writer and editor with a deep portfolio of published work spanning a variety of fields. She has been helping tell the story of the Living Building Challenge and the important efforts of the International Living Future Institute since 2006.

Mary is the author of the debut title in the Living Building Challenge Series, *Building in Bloom: The Making of the Center for Sustainable Landscapes at Phipps Conservatory and Botanical Gardens*. She collaborated with Jason F. McLennan on his collection of essays, *Zugunruhe: The Inner Migration to Profound Environmental Change* and contributed the introduction to his follow-up book, *Transformational Thought: Radical Ideas to Remake the Built Environment.* In addition, she provided editorial support for *Living Building Education: The Evolution of Bertschi School's Science Wing* and *Busby: Architecture's New Edges*, both published by Ecotone. Mary is also the collaborative author, with Andrew Schorr, of *The Web-Savvy Patient: An Insider's Guide to Navigating the Internet When Facing Medical Crisis.*

Mary lives with her husband and two children in the Seattle area, where she is always on the lookout for whales in the water and eagles in the trees.

Photo: Jonathan Payne

7

PART I

Foundational Change

The Building's Backstory

9

Part I: **FOUNDATIONAL CHANGE**

Dorothy Stimson Bullitt, member of the
Soroptimist Club of Seattle, ca. 1920s
*Photo: McBride and Anderson / University
of Washington Special Collections*

A MEDIA PIONEER WITH ALTRUISTIC FAMILY VALUES

Dorothy Stimson Bullitt was raised to believe in the power of philanthropy, carefully taught that wealth and influence should be used to serve the greater good.

Brought up in affluence made possible by her father's logging and real estate interests throughout the Pacific Northwest, Dorothy Stimson married attorney A. Scott Bullitt in 1918 at the age of twenty-six. Following her husband's death fourteen years later, Dorothy used her business savvy to create a Seattle-based radio and television empire — the KING Broadcasting Company — beginning in the 1940s, which led to dramatic growth of her personal wealth. She started the Bullitt Foundation in 1952 as a way to give back to the people and culture of the region she loved, and to involve her adult children — Charles Stimson "Stim" Bullitt, Priscilla "Patsy" Bullitt Collins, and Harriet Overton Bullitt — in that process.

Dorothy followed in her mother's philanthropic footsteps: the Foundation supported local cultural, historic, educational, and social causes through its first decade. As the organization matured and its assets became more substantial, the Bullitts agreed to expand its horizons. At Stimson's recommendation,

the Foundation became increasingly involved in conservation issues beginning in the 1970s, pledging funds to public and private entities in and around the Pacific Northwest for land preservation efforts. Notes from a special meeting held in November 1972 among Dorothy and her children indicate their decision to begin committing funds "for the protection of the physical environment within the State of Washington."[1]

After Dorothy passed away in 1989, the Foundation's base grew significantly. By the early 1990s, the endowment reached $100 million. It was time to introduce executive leadership equipped not just to manage the organization's now considerable grantmaking capabilities but also to reflect its sharpening environmental focus. Following a national search overseen by Stimson Bullitt, Patsy Bullitt Collins, and board member Doug Raff, the Foundation found its ideal steward in Denis Hayes.

1   Bullitt Foundation board member Doug Raff refers to this archived transcription in his *Early History of the Bullitt Foundation.*

Photo: David Hiller

HAYES AT THE HELM

Denis Hayes was named president and CEO of the Bullitt Foundation in March 1992, bringing a combination of professional credentials and personal interests in environmental advocacy.

While he may best be known as national coordinator of the first Earth Day when he was a 25-year-old graduate student — and for his subsequent work to spread Earth Day to 180 other nations — Hayes built a diverse resume in the years before he came to the Bullitt Foundation. Under President Carter, Hayes directed the Solar Energy Research Institute (now the National Renewable Energy Laboratory) before going on to teach energy engineering and human ecology at Stanford University, practice law in Silicon Valley, lobby, write, speak, and volunteer — all in service to the environment.

Throughout his adult life, Hayes has been fascinated by what is now referred to as urban ecology: learning from nature to design healthier "ecosystems for people." When considering the Bullitt position, he was drawn to the Foundation's commitment to conservation and endangered species protection, and he appreciated that its efforts were focused in the region where he was raised. (Hayes grew up in Camas, Washington near Portland, Oregon.) More importantly, he found an openness to sponsoring causes that benefit human environments alongside its historic concerns with the natural environment.

When he first arrived at the Foundation, Hayes led efforts to infuse more human causes into the organization's environmental giving strategy. His goal was to strike a better funding balance between grantees dealing with ecosystems and those dealing with people. Gradually, as new foundations cropped up throughout the Cascadia region, it became clear that wildlife conservation was being well supported while urban environmental issues garnered less funding attention. The Bullitt Foundation, Hayes determined, could carve out a uniquely powerful role in the field of urban ecology.

Guided by Hayes, the Foundation made a conscious transition to emphasize the urban landscape in its giving strategies. Since initiating that shift, the organization has made many funding decisions based on the answer to two simple questions: 1) Does this help protect the watersheds and ecosystems that are immediately relevant to the Cascadia region (Seattle, Portland, Vancouver, Anchorage, Spokane, and Boise)?, and 2) Will this help create healthy, creative, vibrant, prosperous cities — models of sustainability and resilience?

Photo: Nic Lehoux

"I liked that the Foundation wanted to address issues that were urgent and that could be influenced with the level of resources available to it. The Bullitt board recognized that profound changes were needed and that big changes often take time. My board has always been more nimble and more patient than most other foundation boards, as long as I can honestly show that progress is being made and that success is still possible."

DENIS HAYES
Bullitt Foundation

"People around the planet are migrating into cities almost like herds of wildebeests across the Serengeti. The United Nations forecasts that two billion more people will move into cities over the next 30 years. Tragically, many of those cities are gigantic slums, deeply polluted and socially dysfunctional. Creating cities that are genuine models of resilience and sustainability would be a hugely valuable thing to do. Ideally, leaders from around the world would learn from our successes and failures."

DENIS HAYES
Bullitt Foundation

"Cascadia is the greenest, best-educated, most progressive corner of the wealthiest country in human history. If we couldn't create models of urban sustainability here, it would be hard to remain hopeful about the human prospect."

DENIS HAYES
Bullitt Foundation

13

"We started talking about the idea of a new building, wondering how we might use our assets to create a model that people could emulate. Not just a signature or a vanity building, but a structure that was intended to be something anyone could take lessons from and build themselves."

MAGGIE WALKER
Former Bullitt Foundation Board Chair

Stimson-Green Mansion circa 1914
Photo: Washington Trust for Historic Preservation

The Carriage House circa 1911
Photo: Washington Trust for Historic Preservation

14

THE SEARCH FOR A NEW HOME

In 1989, the Bullitt Foundation moved its offices from the KING Broadcasting building to the Carriage House at the stately Stimson-Green Mansion, where Dorothy lived as a child and which her daughter Patsy Bullitt Collins had recently acquired. It was in those quarters where Denis Hayes first got to work on the Foundation's behalf.

Although the family's ties to the property created a sentimental backdrop for the headquarters and the rent-free lease was fiscally advantageous, the space was ill-suited to the organization's needs. The Carriage House was just that, designed to function as a series of stalls and a hayloft, not an office. With low ceilings, antique windows, and no insulation, it was cold in the winter and hot in the summer with high electric bills throughout the year. When Patsy gifted the property to the Washington Trust for Historic Preservation in 2001, it triggered a new five-year lease for the Foundation, which prompted Hayes and the board to reevaluate the wisdom of staying long-term.

The Foundation was now sharply focused on human ecology, including an entire program devoted to energy and climate change. Operating out of an extremely inefficient building with exorbitant energy bills per square foot did not jibe with the organization's fundamental

tenets. Hayes convinced the board to initiate a search for greener pastures, with the plan being to move at the end of the Carriage House lease into new rented offices that reflected the Foundation's environmental mission and values.

But when they looked for such a space, nothing they saw met their criteria. Some rentable buildings were advertised as "green" but would have required considerable refurbishing to get the Bullitt offices to their desired level of sustainability. Other options were too far removed from Seattle's downtown core. Still others posed serious seismic risk.

Soon, Hayes began to float the idea of building a new structure that could be custom-fit with the types of sustainable features and systems the Foundation supported. The organization had an opportunity to create something that could serve as a green demonstration piece for the region.

TO BUILD OR NOT TO BUILD

The Bullitt Foundation trustees wrestled at length with the idea of building a new headquarters because they knew it needed to be much more than an environmentally sophisticated structure.

If they were going to draw deeply from their asset base to finance the monumental effort, the resulting building had to serve the organization's financial and programmatic objectives. In addition to exploring the cutting edge of design, technology, and behavior, it also needed to change building codes and manufacturing processes. The board approached the decision-making process collaboratively and thoroughly, carefully weighing all advantages and disadvantages.

Those who resisted the idea argued that the board's responsibility was to oversee and protect the institution's resources; the proposed building would cost substantially more than a conventional structure but — at least for many years — reflect no greater market value. They feared that it might turn out to be an expensive exercise in symbolism that did not make financial sense.

Supporters argued the reverse. The Bullitt Foundation is a philanthropy with a purpose, they maintained. It exists not to accumulate wealth, but to create attractive new models of sustainability. What the proposed building could offer in terms of public education would have far more impact than academic studies or advocacy work funded for the same amount of money.

After months of deliberation, Harriet Bullitt expressed her support of the plan to build, stating that her family created its fortune not by being timid but by being bold and taking calculated risks. Once she weighed in, the opposition melted away. (The heart of the debate did not occur until there were preliminary cost estimates for the project, so she did not officially endorse the decision until that time.) When Harriet blessed the plan, the seed of the Bullitt Center was effectively planted.

"I never doubted that Harriet would support the Bullitt Center, and she revealed her enthusiasm at precisely the moment when she knew it would be most influential. In private conversations, she expressed her support for the project in deeply personal terms. She was supporting me as much as the concept of the Bullitt Center. I, in turn, resolved to do whatever was necessary to make sure that the building achieved its sky-high goals. In addition to all my personal and environmental motivations, I was determined not to let Harriet down."

DENIS HAYES
Bullitt Foundation

"There are people who would argue that being prudent with your endowment is, of course, what you have to do with your investments. But making the big expenditure that is going to be transformative in some positive way is even more important. Stim Bullitt used to argue that the Foundation didn't exist to preserve money; it existed to do good."

DOUG RAFF
Bullitt Foundation Board Member

"Creating change and creating great things in the community: that's what the Bullitt family intended when they set up the Foundation. We honored that when we chose to build this building."

MAGGIE WALKER
Former Bullitt Foundation Board Chair

"I was very cool to the idea of this building at the beginning. I thought it was going to be an expensive and complicated nightmare. But the more I learned about it, the more I thought it could really happen, especially if Denis was behind it. He doesn't start things that don't work. He does not expect failures and he doesn't get them."

HARRIET BULLITT

15

INSISTING ON THE HIGHEST STANDARD

Once the decision was made to build, Hayes considered various approaches that would ensure the future headquarters would be designed and constructed to the highest possible standards — particularly around energy performance — and would serve as a profound example of what types of sustainable systems are feasible in present and future urban environments.

He was drawn to Leadership in Energy and Environmental Design (LEED®) Platinum and its promise of energy efficiency, but he knew that unpredictable plug loads and tenant behaviors often compromised LEED buildings' actual performance. When other green building standards also fell short of what he wanted, Hayes reconciled himself to defining his own set of rigorous objectives then going out in search of architects and engineers capable of designing to those goals.

Just as Hayes was giving up hope of finding a building standard that reflected his bold vision for the project, he was introduced in 2007 to Jason F. McLennan and the Living Building Challenge. McLennan, CEO of the Cascadia Green Building Council (and the organization that would later become the International Living Future Institute[2]), was meeting with Program Officer Amy Solomon at the Stimson-Green Carriage House to promote the Living Building Challenge as a worthy recipient of Bullitt Foundation funding. He pitched the Challenge as the greenest building standard in the world, capable of creating a "Living" built environment filled with net zero energy, net zero water structures made from non-toxic locally sourced materials. Living Buildings, McLennan explained, are as nurturing, efficient, and beautiful as a flower. Upon hearing McLennan's impassioned description of Living Buildings, Solomon knew that Hayes needed to join the conversation.

McLennan went on to explain the revolutionary concept to Hayes in greater detail. To earn full Living Building

certification, he said, a project must demonstrate twelve months of operational performance according to twenty Imperatives distributed among seven "Petal" areas:[3]

SITE: RESTORING A HEALTHY COEXISTENCE WITH NATURE

WATER: CREATING WATER INDEPENDENT SITES, BUILDINGS, AND COMMUNITIES

ENERGY: RELYING ONLY ON CURRENT SOLAR INCOME

HEALTH: MAXIMIZING PHYSICAL AND PSYCHOLOGICAL HEALTH AND WELL-BEING

MATERIALS: ENDORSING PRODUCTS AND PROCESSES THAT ARE SAFE FOR ALL SPECIES THROUGH TIME

EQUITY: SUPPORTING A JUST, EQUITABLE WORLD

BEAUTY: CELEBRATING DESIGN THAT CREATES TRANSFORMATIVE CHANGE

Hayes knew he had found the roadmap for the Foundation's new headquarters. The Living Building Challenge overlaid beautifully with everything he hoped to achieve with the project, specifically in how it would allow the organization to create and operate out of a building that honored the ways in which nature organizes itself. So McLennan left the Bullitt Foundation offices that day having met more than a future source of foundation grants: he had encountered a future Living Building owner, a future board member of the International Living Future Institute, a future landlord, and a future friend.

Although the Bullitt Foundation did not officially register its project with the International Living Building Institute until March 8, 2010 (the 53rd project to do so after the Living Building Challenge was formally launched in November 2006), Hayes knew he wanted to pursue it as soon as he had finished reading the full text of the Challenge.

2   The International Living Building Institute was formed in 2009. Its name was changed to the International Living Future Institute in 2011.

3   The original 2006 version of the Standard had only six Petal areas and 16 Imperatives, then referred to as "Prerequisites." The Bullitt Center registered in 2010 under Version 2.0 of the Living Building Challenge and was certified in 2015 under Version 2.1.

> **"THE LIVING BUILDING CHALLENGE ABSOLUTELY REFLECTS THE MISSION OF THE BULLITT FOUNDATION. CREATING A BUILT ENVIRONMENT THAT FUNCTIONS LIKE A NATURAL ECOSYSTEM HAS BEEN RIGHT SMACK IN MY SWEET SPOT SINCE THE MID-1960S, AND IT HAS BECOME MORE AND MORE THE SWEET SPOT OF THE FOUNDATION."**
>
> **DENIS HAYES,** Bullitt Foundation

"Amy Solomon mentioned that Bullitt was contemplating a building project as part of its increasing interest in urban ecology. So I met with Denis, he shared what he hoped he could achieve, and I told him it was a project we would have a great interest in. I didn't realize at the time that he was interviewing prospective project managers for the building."

CHRIS ROGERS
Point 32

"Chris Rogers and Chris Faul became the project's developers, working closely with Denis and supervising this process. They were a great choice. I don't know anyone else who could have done what they did, particularly when it came to dealing with regulatory matters and with government structures."

DOUG RAFF
Bullitt Foundation Board Member

A DEVELOPING PARTNERSHIP

Foundation Program Officer Amy Solomon helped connect key players once again by introducing Hayes to Chris Rogers, who had recently overseen the creation of the Olympic Sculpture Park on behalf of the Seattle Art Museum. Rogers was opening a sustainability-oriented development company called Point 32 with several colleagues, and the team was looking for projects that would complement their vision of sustainability and quality within the urban setting. Solomon correctly assumed that Rogers would be eager to hear of the Foundation's plans.

Hayes and Rogers hit it off quickly, with Rogers expressing such interest in the proposed project that he volunteered to help research potential building sites along with his Point 32 partner, Chris Faul, who brought significant construction and engineering experience to the endeavor. Soon, Hayes formally named Point 32 as the Foundation's development partner and "the Chrises," as they came to be known, led the search for a suitable location for the Foundation's new headquarters.

17

Denis Hayes and
Jason F. McLennan

> *"The site had a number of wonderful attributes. It would be convenient to the vibrant Capitol Hill neighborhood with its bus and trolley lines and a light rail coming in, it was on the most important east-west bus route from the downtown business district, and it had zoning that would restrict any building to its south from being so tall that we'd have to worry about something shading our solar roof."*
>
> **DENIS HAYES**
> Bullitt Foundation

THE WHERE, WHAT, AND HOW

Point 32 began its work with a dual assignment: to find a site for the project while simultaneously evaluating the principles of the Living Building Challenge. The nature of the Standard's rigorous Imperatives disqualified certain sites, as did zoning restrictions, listing prices, and distance from Seattle's urban core. Hayes, Rogers, and Faul determined that the ideal site would offer:

- Exceptional solar exposure

- Proximity to downtown Seattle

- Easy access to existing and planned public transportation

- Zoning that would accommodate mid-rise construction

- High visibility

It did not take long for Rogers and Faul to locate — and see the potential in — the five-sided, western-facing lot rimmed by East Madison Street, East Pike Street, and 15th Avenue. (A small public park completes the point of the triangle formed by the lot.) When Hayes saw the site, whose prominent location atop Seattle's lively Capitol Hill offered both solar and social advantages, he was convinced. Before committing to it, he asked McLennan to take a look to assess the site's Living Building Challenge readiness. McLennan, too, could see the promise of the lot and encouraged Hayes to proceed. In April 2008, the Cascadia Center for Sustainable Design and Construction (a Bullitt Foundation subsidiary that had been created to be the legal owner of the building) finalized its purchase of the property. The future Bullitt Center had an address.

A modest one-story structure used by C.C. Attle's formerly occupied the property connecting East Madison Street, East Pike Street, and 15th Avenue in Seattle.
Photo: The Miller Hull Partnership

"I remember first seeing the lot and in that moment thinking that maybe we could start something really powerful here on this modest site. It was a little piece of magic that offered the potential to breed something even greater; to be regenerative."

JASON F. MCLENNAN
International Living Future Institute

19

THE GREENEST BUILDING

The future home of the Bullitt Center showed enormous potential from every angle.
Photos: The Miller Hull Partnership

MODELING POSSIBILITY

Even before the architectural and engineering plans for the building began to take shape, the Foundation knew it was embarking on a transformative endeavor — one that would join together the altruistic instincts of the Bullitt family and the fervent environmental passion of Denis Hayes with the bold vision of the Living Building Challenge. The Bullitt Center would be an asset that would allow the Foundation to speak with authority about what is possible on the urban landscape. There was never any doubt that the future headquarters would rely fully on solar energy, and if a mid-rise structure in the cloudiest major American city can draw enough energy from the sun for all its power, Hayes asserted, then this one building might be enough to convince the energy-hungry world that solar energy is a rich resource.

With a clear and purposeful resolve to exceed currently accepted boundaries of sustainable building design, and a favorable site on which to do so, the Bullitt Foundation pressed forward with its progressive and leading edge plans. It was time to hand-pick the individuals who would not just design and build the Bullitt Center, but help turn it into a powerful lever for substantive change.

21

PART II

Breaking New Ground

The Players, the Process, and the Plan

Photo: Nic Lehoux

ONLY

23

THE GREENEST BUILDING

Photo: Nic Lehoux

GETTING STARTED

Planning for the Bullitt Center began in earnest in the summer
of 2008. Denis Hayes and Point 32 had brought University
of Washington Architecture Department faculty member
Robert Peña onto the project as a way of adding an academic
voice to the discussions.[4] The small but dedicated team, which
gradually expanded as Peña invited graduate students to attend,
met weekly to review sustainable building topics and assess
which state-of-the-art strategies would be most effective in
creating an ultra-high-performance mid-rise structure.

25

4   In 1981, Peña worked as a summer intern studying national renewable energy
strategies at the Solar Energy Research Institute (now the National Renewable
Energy Laboratory) where Denis Hayes served as director. Three weeks into
Peña's internship, Hayes resigned the post in protest of President Reagan's energy
policies. Before leaving, though, Hayes made a lasting impression on Peña, who
still refers to him as "a longstanding hero of mine." The professional path that later
brought Peña to Seattle included a five-year stint during the 1990s on the faculty
at the University of Oregon, where Jason F. McLennan was one of his students.

"We wanted people who weren't just saying the right things about sustainability, but had done projects that strongly expressed those values. They needed to really care about the quality of their work; failures of craftsmanship could doom the building's performance. Finally, they all had to play well with others. We had no room for prima donnas on the team, and we rejected some enormously talented people who appeared to be interested only in their own ideas. We were trying to do something that had never been done before, and I needed to have the architects, engineers, contractors, subcontractors, and professors all listening to and challenging one another."

DENIS HAYES
Bullitt Foundation

TALENT SCOUTS

By fall of 2008, the core team, led by Hayes and Point 32's Chris Rogers, initiated a formal search for designers, engineers, and builders equipped to take on the Bullitt Center project.

They sought firms that met certain criteria that would benefit the whole endeavor, specifically those with:

- Roots in the Cascadia region (Seattle, Portland, or Vancouver)

- Passion for the challenge of designing and constructing the first major commercial Living Building in the world

- Extensive experience in sustainable design and construction

- Knowledge and appreciation of regional aesthetics and materials

- Enthusiasm about working via an integrated process with other disciplines

- Professional pride unobstructed by ego

Meanwhile, Peña and his colleague, Professor Carrie Sturts Dossick from the University of Washington Construction Management Department, organized a design studio composed of teams of eight students who went about conceptualizing the Bullitt Center. As the search continued for the best professional architects for the project, the UW students spent the winter 2009 academic term crafting plans for three different possible designs for the building.[5]

Not surprisingly, word spread quickly among the professions that a cutting-edge project in Seattle would soon go through a design team selection process. Many of the region's leading firms expressed interest by reaching out casually or formally to Hayes, Rogers, or McLennan. Some even offered to provide feedback on the design studio concepts developed by Peña's students as a way of getting on board, although doing so did not prove to give anyone a competitive edge.

The search committee followed a more-or-less traditional process of reviewing candidates and creating a shortlist of finalists. The architecture firm was named first, followed by the engineers and the builder (which was a slight departure from the common practice of architects and engineers teaming up to pursue a project jointly). Along the way, Rogers asked all finalists to name the firms from the other disciplines that they felt would excel at the project and be good collaborative partners.

The process continued for several months. When the list of architecture firms was winnowed to fewer than ten, Hayes, Rogers, and Point 32's Chris Faul, along with an advisory council they had assembled, went out in spring 2009 to meet each at their place of business and to tour at least one completed building the firm had designed using green methods.

5 Although none of these plans was used in its entirety, there were some commonalities between what the students conceptualized and what Miller Hull eventually came up with.

The entire team at The Miller Hull Partnership was on hand to greet the Bullitt Center selection committee when they visited the architects' offices. *Photo: The Miller Hull Partnership*

"Every major architecture firm in the region wanted to land this project. The Living Building Challenge is driven by architects who are repeatedly frustrated by their desire to do something that's exceptional in terms of performance and design, only to find the high-performance aspects value-engineered out. The promise of a major project that would be driven by performance goals, rather than by maximizing rates of return, stirred up everyone's creative instincts."

DENIS HAYES
Bullitt Foundation

"We started by naming the architect, since we felt the project really needed a design vision. But we didn't want to support the formation of forced marriages, especially because we were pursuing an integrated design approach. We limited our pool of prospective engineers to firms Miller Hull said it most enjoyed and respected."

CHRIS ROGERS
Point 32

"Beyond Miller Hull's interest in sustainability, they espoused a practice of working with wood that we felt represented a Northwest design vernacular that's climate-responsive."

CHRIS ROGERS
Point 32

"Every step we'd taken up to the point when we were selected for the Bullitt Center project prepared us to take on this building. The day we got it, I said to everyone in the office, 'We're about to change the world.'"

RON ROCHON
The Miller Hull Partnership

"I think Denis really tuned into PAE when he saw that EUI document and thought about achieving those numbers. It really got the dialogue going between us and it was the first time I saw that twinkle in his eye."

PAUL SCHWER
PAE

"PAE emerged quickly as a strong thought leader, and we knew they would provide a balance to the architecture side of the project. They were equals at the design table when thinking about things like systems, orientation, and passive airflow."

CHRIS FAUL
Point 32

A DEEP GREEN TEAM

ARCHITECTS

The Seattle-based Miller Hull Partnership rose to the top of the list of potential architects for numerous reasons. Its rich portfolio of sustainable design work, particularly its leadership in passive solar design, assured Hayes and Rogers that the firm had the requisite expertise to achieve the project's primary goals along with the necessary curiosity to expand its knowledge base into new areas of sustainable design. The firm's previous work, notable for its aesthetic appeal, also proved its ability to skillfully combine beauty and performance. The impressive fact that all fifty Miller Hull employees came out to greet the selection committee when they visited in the final phase of the selection process demonstrated the firm's deeply aligned commitment. They understood that the Bullitt Center project would be a team-wide effort and they were eager to take on the challenge ... and the Challenge.

ENGINEERS

PAE was chosen to oversee the engineering strategies for the Bullitt Center not only because of the firm's previous successful collaborations with Miller Hull, but also because of its well-documented history of effectively engaging in integrated processes to achieve cutting-edge sustainable solutions.

After Chris Faul conducted an initial screening with President Paul Schwer in PAE's Portland headquarters, Schwer traveled to Seattle to meet with Hayes in what was billed as a casual introduction but evolved quickly into a preliminary interview. Although Schwer was told not to prepare anything, he had made a last-minute decision to bring along a document mapping out the levels of energy use intensity (EUI) he thought might be attainable in an ultra-efficient mid-rise office building in downtown Seattle. Once the rough EUI calculations were presented, Hayes suddenly became much more engaged in the conversation. To this day, Schwer credits that document with helping PAE land the Bullitt Center job.

> *"Schuchart had a strong local construction legacy and was already involved in several other civic-oriented projects, which offered a nice tie-in."*

CHRIS ROGERS
Point 32

> *"It was clear from the start that this would be a special project. Given our passion for sustainability within the built environment, we immediately said yes to the opportunity and asked what we could do to support the effort."*

CASEY SCHUCHART
Schuchart

BUILDERS

Schuchart was named the project's general contractor because of its deep Seattle roots, its good standing in the green building industry, and its family-run operational framework. Point 32 had previously worked with Schuchart, and Rogers and Faul strongly vouched for the firm to Hayes, who had less confidence in his ability to judge contractors than architects and engineers.

President George Schuchart, along with his son, Division Manager Casey Schuchart, and Project Manager Christian LaRocco were also eager to participate in an integrated design and planning process, which is not true for all builders. Rather than wait to step in after design schematics were completed, Schuchart representatives attended weekly planning charrettes beginning in mid-2009, during which time the architects and engineers were still discussing and debating all aspects of building and systems design.

"The whole concept of planned obsolescence is offensive. Planned obsolescence in a building – given the massive investment of time and resources that goes into a building – is unconscionable."

DENIS HAYES
Bullitt Foundation

"Some of the most sustainable buildings in the world are those that are never taken down. So when Denis proposed a 250-year structure, though with a skin that might need to be shed once or twice – like a snake sheds its skin – it got us thinking about something bigger than a single building project."

RON ROCHON
The Miller Hull Partnership

"I constantly urged the design team to abandon all preconceptions. Yes, the Bullitt Center would have to have a roof; it rains a lot in Seattle. But they needed to start with a nearly blank canvas. To provide the comfort, power, visibility, electricity, water, and other services that tenants demand within the design constraints of the Challenge required that the team felt free to be as radically different as necessary. We went down a lot of dead ends in the process, but we ultimately found elegant solutions to all the problems."

DENIS HAYES
Bullitt Foundation

DEFINING THE MISSION

With the core team in place, the first order of business was to ensure that all the players understood that Hayes was very serious about meeting all the Petals of the Living Building Challenge. By itself, that would arguably pose the toughest design challenge ever faced by an integrated design team.

However, Hayes wanted to go farther; he wanted to be net energy positive. He wanted an emphasis on durable materials that were also healthy and local. He wanted the Bullitt Center to have an "irresistible staircase" that would provide tenants a delightful way to get a little more exercise.

In order for the project to succeed, it would need to embody new conceptual approaches to urban design and construction that would remain relevant for generations.

Hayes was so focused on durability as an underlying goal of the project that he specifically instructed the team to design the Bullitt Center to last at least 250 years. If the stone structures on the campuses of Oxford and Cambridge have stood for six centuries, why couldn't a modern urban mid-rise be designed to endure more than the standard 50 years? Clearly, the Bullitt Center would not be constructed of granite nor designed to

withstand armed conflicts. Still, Hayes reiterated the value of creating a highly resilient building that would become an important part of the Foundation's enduring wealth, not a mere financial transaction with a beginning and an end determined by financial discount rates. If, in 1379 when Oxford University set up its newest constituent college (aptly named New College), it had calculated the discounted cash value of those buildings 635 years hence, the answer would have been zero no matter what discount rate they used. But would anyone argue that the Oxford campus has zero value today? Buildings should not be elements of a throw-away economy, Hayes argued. The Bullitt Center needed to be designed and built to last far beyond present-day conventions. He maintained — to the project team and to his board — that the building's value would increase over time as resources dwindle and net zero structures emerge as the only reasonable options in the built environment.

31

EMBRACING THE CHALLENGE

The chosen architects, engineers, and general contractor knew going into the project that it would be designed and built according to the Living Building Challenge with its seven Petals and its twenty Imperatives.

Miller Hull and PAE were familiar with the Challenge, though neither firm had direct experience pursuing it on any project. Schuchart first learned of the Challenge when they joined the Bullitt project. Indeed, when the Bullitt Center team was formed in mid-2009, only three aspirational Living Building Challenge projects had been completed,[6] only a handful were under construction, and none had yet been certified.

Everybody did their homework to familiarize themselves with the Challenge prior to kicking off the planning stage. Well before the Bullitt Center was designed, it was obvious it would be like no other Living Building that came before it. Projects that previously sought Living Building certification were significantly smaller, located in different climate zones, and intended for such different uses that they offered the Bullitt team almost no frame of reference beyond their shared building standard. There were scattered buildings around North America that were planned as Living Buildings but those either never got built or only achieved net zero status. That would not be the case with the Bullitt Center, whose owner and developer were adamant that the intended Living goal be met. It had to perform to those seven performance area Petals. Period. As such, with no precedent to which they could compare their ideas, the design team had a responsibility to create nothing less than the highest-performing mid-rise structure on the planet.

6 By June 2009, only ten projects had registered as aspirational Living Buildings. The first three projects audited for certification were the Omega Center in Rhinebeck, NY; the Tyson Living Learning Center in St. Louis, MO; and the Eco-Sense House in Victoria, BC. All three were in their mandatory 12-month pre-certification operational review period in 2009. Omega and Tyson went on to earn full Living Building certification in fall 2010; Eco-Sense was certified for four of the six Petals included in Version 1.3 of the Challenge.

"Achieving an unprecedented level of energy efficiency that involved not just the structure of the building but also the behavior of the people inside seemed to me to be the toughest challenge we faced. Relying on locally-sourced materials that posed no threat to the health of humans or other living things was a pretty close second. I had no doubt that we could collect enough rainwater in Seattle to meet our needs, though the legal and regulatory hurdles to letting people drink treated rainwater proved surprisingly stubborn."

DENIS HAYES
Bullitt Foundation

"Many aspects of the building – like the choice of site, the choice of materials, the aesthetic elements – were one-shot events. You needed to do it right, and then you could put it behind you. But energy and water were focused on future performance. For its entire lifetime, the Bullitt Center would have to produce as much energy and water as it used. So we started with the energy system and the water system and designed the building around them."

CHRIS FAUL
Point 32

NET ZERO OR NOTHING

While Living Buildings can only be certified if all twenty Imperatives are met across all seven Petals, the Bullitt Center design team knew that two performance areas would drive the perceived success of the entire effort: net zero energy and net zero water. In other words, if they accomplished everything else but fell short of achieving net zero performance — particularly with regard to energy — the project would be considered a failure, by the public and by the owner.

The building's location in rainy Seattle offered an abundance of one resource and a scarcity of another. Plenty of precipitation meant that engineers had to worry less about water inventory and more about disposal strategies. But the clouds delivering that rain hovered between the building and the sunbeams needed to power the solar panels. It was critical that the team work collaboratively on designs that prioritized the two net zero objectives while also allowing all other performance concerns to fall into place behind them.

BUILDING LIFE CYCLE

250 YEAR STRUCTURE
HEAVY TIMBER, CONCRETE & STEEL

50 YEAR SKIN
HIGH PERFORMANCE ENVELOPE

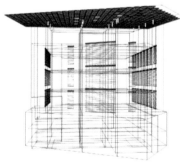

25 YEAR TECHNOLOGY
ACTIVE SOLAR CONTROL
PHOTOVOLTAICS

NET ZERO WATER

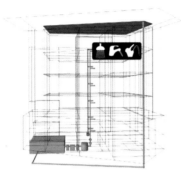

RAINWATER COLLECTION
100% DEMAND MET ON SITE
50,000 GALLON CISTERN

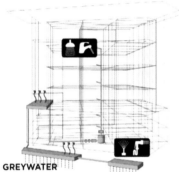

GREYWATER
100% TREATMENT ON SITE
EVAPOTRANSPIRATION & INFILTRATION

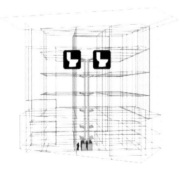

WASTE COMPOST
100% TREATMENT ON SITE

NET ZERO ENERGY

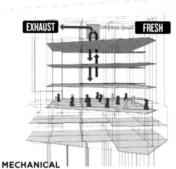

MECHANICAL
GROUND SOURCE HEAT EXCHANGE
RADIANT HEATING/COOLING
HEAT RECOVERY AIR SYSTEM

NATURAL VENTILATION
NIGHT FLUSH & OPERABLE WINDOWS

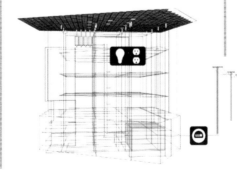

ENERGY
100% RENEWABLE ON SITE
GRID USED AS BATTERY

OCCUPANT

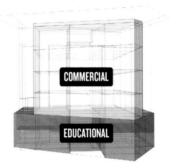

PROGRAM
OCCUPANCY
PRIVATE USERS ABOVE, PUBLIC FOCUS
USERS AT GRADE

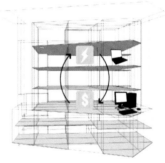

INTERNAL CAP & TRADE
EACH TENANT HAS AN ENERGY BUDGET;
UNUSED ENERGY CAN BE TRANSFERRED

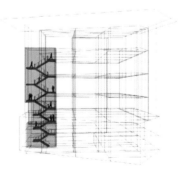

IRRESISTIBLE STAIR
ELEVATOR ALTERNATIVE, HEALTHIER
OCCUPANTS, ENGAGEMENT WITH STREET

Graphic: The Miller Hull Partnership

35

Point 32's Chris Faul (second from left) and Chris Rogers (far right) lead a tour for Rosen Plevneliev, President of Bulgaria (second from right), who visited the Bullitt Center site in May 2012. *Photo: John Stamets*

36

"At the end of the first charrette, the first thing Denis asked me was, 'What else you got?' We'd been in a room with fifty incredibly smart people for two days, so I couldn't believe he was asking that. But it made me think, 'What else DO I have?' That happened a lot. It taught us to ask ourselves, 'We have these great systems, but what else can we do?'"

PAUL SCHWER
PAE

"The idea of the first charrette was less about design by committee, at least with regard to the form of the building, and more about getting aspirations on the table that the design team could chew on."

ROB PEÑA
Integrated Design Lab

"We had a pretty good handle on high-performance concepts and principles going into the first charrette. As far as design, we got about 80 percent of the way there in those first two days. The rest of it was fitting it into the budget and making it replicable for other developers."

RON ROCHON
The Miller Hull Partnership

THE FIRST CHARRETTE

The initial all-hands planning charrette took place in the Miller Hull offices on June 1-2, 2009. Following the Living Building Challenge guidelines requiring an integrated design process, every key player on the project's design-build team was present.

Representatives of the City of Seattle and the community were also in attendance, as were various specialists and practitioners personally invited by Hayes and McLennan because of the expertise they could lend to the process. Unlike typical design charrettes, where architects guide the discussion, this and all subsequent Bullitt Center planning sessions featured a diverse cast of informed, vocal, and engaged participants.

By that point, the team had determined that all six floors of the Bullitt Center would be used exclusively for office space. (Hayes and Point 32 had previously explored the possibility of incorporating residential and retail components into the building — in fact, Hayes hoped to live in the building — but the mixed-use plan was abandoned before the first design charrette. The neighborhood surrounding the site was already well stocked with residential properties and retail outlets but it was very short on office inventory. An all-office model would fill a more pressing neighborhood need.)

The intent of the two-day gathering was to hear ideas from all parties about how to design and build a structure whose depth of performance was unprecedented. Given the complexities of the systems, PAE and Miller Hull came to the charrette equipped with preliminary data they had calculated would be needed to meet various performance targets. Having the data in hand created a helpful framework for the brainstorming process that followed.

During the first day, participants broke into Petal-specific groups to capture every possible idea and concern. Then, Miller Hull synthesized the day's ideas and converted them that evening into sketches that were used to initiate and inform the second day's discussions. The architects followed the same process the second evening so that when the two-day event came to a close, a rough generative diagram for the building had emerged.

37

"The planning process was driven by what needed to get done. Our meetings were a wonderful mixture of creativity and discipline. What were our options? What did we need to decide today? And what commitments did each of us need to make to keep everything on track?" Margaret Sprug brought a new checklist to each meeting, and we left two hours later with another dozen decisions behind us."

DENIS HAYES
Bullitt Foundation

"PAE and Miller Hull became really close on this project. There are a lot of great firms that we've worked with and that design great buildings, but the relationship doesn't always have that zing to it. Everyone on this project, including the owner and the construction team, just got along so well. Everyone knew from early on that we were going to be part of something special."

PAUL SCHWER
PAE

"I was struck by how disciplined this design team was. On other projects, I've observed a lot of 'distracted by shiny object' behavior, but that was never the case here. It was, 'Investigate, make a determination, make a decision, move on.'"

ROB PEÑA
Integrated Design Lab

In the spirit of reuse, the sign from Schuchart's construction site office was fashioned into a whimsical sitting area table by NK Build, a Seattle craftsman firm that also created the spectacular conference room table (featured on page 139) that graces the sixth-floor conference room. A living wall provides the final decorative touch. *Photo: Brent Smith*

"Having the contractors participate in the planning process was extremely important as we needed to complete the Bullitt Center at a reasonable budget. Although meeting the Living Building Challenge was non-negotiable, we needed to drive the project home as economically as possible."

DENIS HAYES
Bullitt Foundation

"It's always our desire to be engaged early because it allows us the opportunity to contribute real value. Making changes at that early stage is a lot less expensive than making them later. As a builder, we're able to leverage the pre-construction engagement toward delivering greater value."

CASEY SCHUCHART
Schuchart

"It was absolutely critical that the contractor for this project was there culturally and philosophically, and that they were passionate about making sure that the building that got delivered was the greenest in the world. Schuchart had a great amount of passion."

MARGARET SPRUG
The Miller Hull Partnership

ONGOING PLANNING

In the weeks and months that followed the first charrette, members of the core team worked individually and in smaller groups to sculpt the building's plans. Subcontractors, consultants, students, community members, and government representatives continued to weigh in with their ideas as well.

Budget meetings were held periodically as the plans unfolded with greater clarity so that the team could explore the easiest, most cost-effective ways to achieve the specific approaches being mapped out. One of the many advantages of involving the builder during this early stage was that Schuchart could provide real-time budget feedback as new ideas were incorporated into the design scheme. If the architects or engineers proposed an approach that Schuchart knew would add considerable cost (especially if the builder was aware of a less expensive solution), the team was in a better position to adapt plans as they went. Aligning the architects' and builders' expertise during planning, rather than asking Schuchart to bid on a completed set of drawings, helped keep the project's first costs in check.

PRIDE OF THE CITY

The lasting success of the Bullitt Center would hinge on the regulatory environment. Even the world's most sophisticated sustainable systems are irrelevant if they are designed into buildings whose city ordinances do not recognize, allow, and encourage them. One of the fundamental intents of the Living Building Challenge has always been to effect change by demonstrating what is possible; the goal of the Bullitt Center has always been to showcase those possibilities on a grander-than-ever scale.

The Bullitt Foundation and Point 32 needed to appeal directly to the City of Seattle and persuade officials not just to approve the Bullitt Center's plans but to laud them. This project, they contended, would permanently and profoundly change the landscape of Seattle's built environment. Being home to the world's greenest office building would prove the city's commitment to sustainability and entice other developers to follow suit.

But the proposed building would be flat-out illegal under the municipal codes that existed when the plans were being finalized. Rather than change the building's plans to harvest its own water, generate its own power, and treat its own waste, Hayes appealed to the city to change its building regulations — not strictly for the Bullitt Center, but for all sustainable structures to come. He met with Mayor Greg Nickels, Deputy

The trees of McGilvra Place Park, the skyline of downtown Seattle, and the peaks of the Olympic Mountains are all visible from the Bullitt Center's sixth floor conference room. *Photo: Dan Farmer*

Mayor Tim Ceis, and Department of Planning and Development Director Diane Sugimura to discuss the merits of the Living Building Challenge, the particulars of the Bullitt Center plan, and the wisdom of adapting to the built environment's changing needs. Codes should be written to reflect what's coming in the future, he asserted, rather than the past.

In late 2009, the City Council voted unanimously to approve a Living Building Pilot Program, which allowed for up to ten demonstration projects (of which the Bullitt Center was the first). Excerpts from the program's original text clarify its purpose:

Living Building Pilot Program[7]

The goal of the Living Building Pilot Program is to encourage the development of buildings that meet the Living Building Challenge by allowing departures from code requirements that might otherwise discourage or prevent buildings from meeting this standard. Overall, the Living Building Pilot Program is intended to:

- Stimulate innovative development that meets the goals of the Living Building Challenge and City of Seattle design guidelines.

- Encourage development that will serve as a model for other projects throughout the City and region and will stimulate development of new Living Buildings.

- Identify barriers to Living Buildings in current codes and processes.

Seattle has continued to amend and improve the program. The city's ongoing willingness to adapt its codes reflects its dual commitment to citizens and to sustainability. Regulators have a fundamental responsibility to maintain basic municipal safety standards, but the new ordinance now allows them to be more flexible about how to meet those objectives. According to Sugimura, the program has prompted richer inter-departmental conversations that have helped the permitting process become more collaborative.

"Green building has been changing and evolving, but the codes were written to address standard buildings and existing, known practices. We told Denis that if he wanted to strive to meet the Living Building Challenge – a high, high bar – then we would allow him flexibility in some of the codes. We wanted to find out what we could learn from these pilot projects; what revisions could be made to the codes on a permanent basis that would remove barriers and help future sustainable projects."

DIANE SUGIMURA
City of Seattle Department of Planning and Development

"The City's Living Building Pilot Program was extremely important in terms of our ability to pursue the Challenge in Seattle under existing codes. It gave us the flexibility to do things that would have otherwise been impossible and illegal. It also established the City's desire to support a groundbreaking project on this scale."

CHRIS ROGERS
Point 32

"The Pilot Program was all about pushing further to help transform the marketplace and encouraging people to try. The first one is the hardest, then the next ones are a bit easier. It takes the first couple of projects like this to prove that it's possible to do it."

DIANE SUGIMURA
City of Seattle Department of Planning and Development

"Diane Sugimura and the City of Seattle and Seattle City Light made that project happen. If the Bullitt Center was anywhere else, it never would have happened because the policy probably wouldn't be accommodative. We had very forward-thinking, innovative city officials from the mayor on down and a progressive municipal utility. They modified their policies to let that building happen."

STEVEN STRONG
Solar Design Associates

7   City of Seattle Legislative Information Service

ON THE MONEY

Getting past regulatory hurdles was an enormous victory for the project. The next sizable challenge was securing financing.

The Foundation needed to find a lender willing to underwrite a project that had no financial precedent. Never before had a commercial building been constructed, engineered to perform, or leased in the same manner. And no appraisal comps existed for a self-sustaining urban structure designed to last 250 years. Whichever institution took on the Bullitt Center had to be comfortable embracing the unknown.

The bottom-line cost to design and build the Bullitt Center was over $30 million. About $18.5 million went toward construction, which is approximately 25 percent higher than a comparably sized standard building on the same lot would have cost to develop. It is important to note that the price tag attached to Living Buildings will decrease as more projects are completed. Some of the Bullitt Center's higher "hard costs," for example, would be lower today as green technologies have since matured and the availability of Challenge-compliant materials has expanded. The project's "soft costs" were high because the design team had to be given ample time to research and create a six-story structure more high performing than anything that came before it, and

additional team members, attorneys, and consultants had to devote significant time interacting with regulatory agencies.

Hayes approached numerous banks seeking financing and only one, U.S. Bank, was prepared to do the project. U.S. Bank had the resources and enthusiasm required to take on what other institutions perceived as too severe a risk. Perhaps most importantly, the bank agreed to finance a project that appraised for far less than it cost to build. Instead of viewing the property as an unsafe real estate investment, they could see its long-term fiscal potential. Just as the Bullitt Center was charting new territory for Seattle's commercial built environment, U.S. Bank was helping the financial industry break important new ground.

In the end, through an extremely complex transaction involving new market tax credits, recovery zone bonds, and some traditional financing, the Bullitt Foundation borrowed more than half of the project's overall costs from U.S. Bank. With funding secured, the Bullitt Center broke ground on August 29, 2011.

Photo: Nic Lehoux

"It took the vision of the people at the Bullitt Foundation and a whole team from the city, the state, and financing partners to make this funding happen. U.S. Bank was just a small part of that transaction. We always knew there would be a way to get there; we just had to work harder until it was done."

BYRON RICHARDS
U.S. Bank

"We had to do all the things a regular developer would have to do, like getting financing and getting tenants and proving that this would be something worth associating with. We worked really hard as a board on all of these issues so people involved wouldn't feel what they were doing was so risky and irresponsible that it might be perceived as inappropriate."

MAGGIE WALKER
Former Bullitt Foundation
Board Chair

"This project gave us an opportunity to invest back in our community in a unique way, so the bank is very excited to be involved."

BYRON RICHARDS
U.S. Bank

PART III

Rooted in the City

Rising to the Petals of the
Living Building Challenge

45

THE GREENEST BUILDING

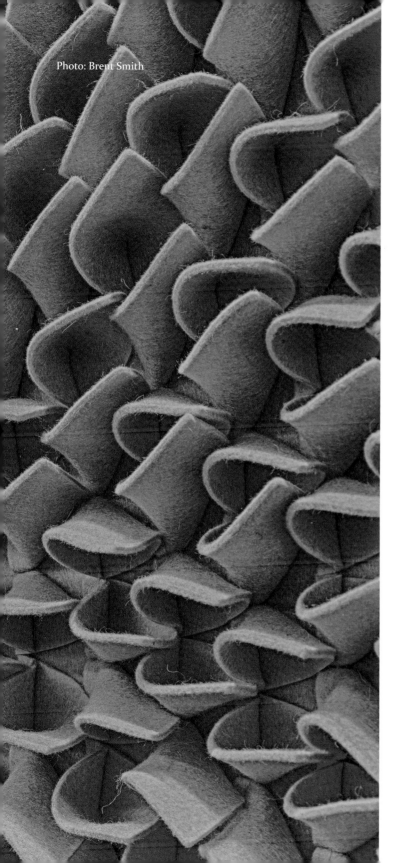

Photo: Brent Smith

"Imagine a building constructed to function as elegantly and efficiently as a flower; a building informed by its bioregion's characteristics, and that generates all of its own energy with renewable resources, captures and treats all of its water, and operates efficiently and for maximum beauty."

LIVING BUILDING CHALLENGE VERSION 2.1

The following chapters of this book focus on the seven individual Petals of the Living Building Challenge Version 2.1:

1. SITE

2. WATER

3. ENERGY

4. HEALTH

5. MATERIALS

6. EQUITY

7. BEAUTY

The chapters are offered here according to the sequence in which they appear in the text of the Challenge, although the process of designing and constructing the Bullitt Center did not follow a linear Petal-by-Petal path. Several features of the building meet the goals of multiple performance areas, so their stories may be found in more than one Petal chapter.

For full text of the Living Building Challenge (including the seven Petals and twenty associated Imperatives of Version 2.1), please visit **living-future.org**.

47

THE
SITE
PETAL

The Place to Be

49

The Site Petal: THE PLACE TO BE

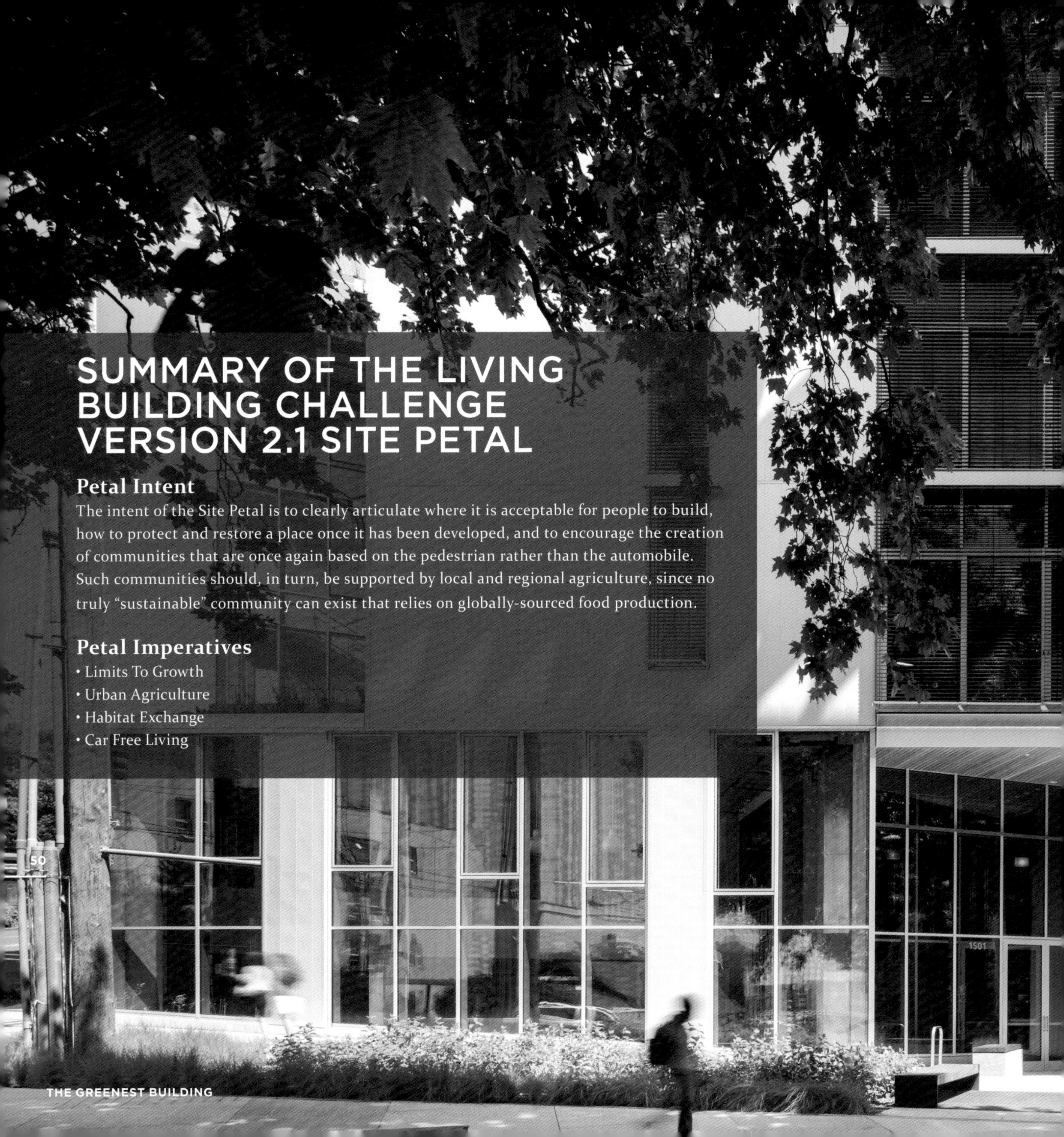

SUMMARY OF THE LIVING BUILDING CHALLENGE VERSION 2.1 SITE PETAL

Petal Intent

The intent of the Site Petal is to clearly articulate where it is acceptable for people to build, how to protect and restore a place once it has been developed, and to encourage the creation of communities that are once again based on the pedestrian rather than the automobile. Such communities should, in turn, be supported by local and regional agriculture, since no truly "sustainable" community can exist that relies on globally-sourced food production.

Petal Imperatives

• Limits To Growth
• Urban Agriculture
• Habitat Exchange
• Car Free Living

A RICH AND GENEROUS SITE

The location at East Madison Street and 15th Avenue provides key assets that support the operational goals of the Bullitt Center:

ACCESSIBILITY. Nearby bus lines, light rail stations, and streetcar routes ensure that occupants and visitors can get to the Bullitt Center from virtually anywhere in the region without having to travel by private automobile.

LIVABILITY. The Capitol Hill neighborhood provides abundant single- and multi-family housing options for current and potential occupants of the Bullitt Center.

WALKABILITY. With a top "walk score" (98 out of a possible 100 points), the building is close to restaurants, cafes, grocery stores, shops, parks, and entertainment venues, rendering a car unnecessary.

LIGHTABILITY. The location enables plenty of unobstructed sunlight to power the rooftop photovoltaics and bathe the interior spaces with natural daylight.

VISIBILITY. Positioned on the downward-facing slope of Capitol Hill, the building offers sweeping views of downtown Seattle and the Olympic Mountains to the west and of Mount Rainier to the south.

BREATHABILITY. McGilvra Place Park and the broad East Madison Street provide the building with a certain amount of elbow room on two sides that would not be possible within the corridors of towers lining Seattle's downtown core.

51

"The site wasn't a shape we would have liked, but we knew that going in. It shows that you don't have to have that prototypical rectangular building with a long south side to achieve net zero energy."

PAUL SCHWER
PAE

"This was a zero lot line, inner-city, five-sided project with adjacent roads, a school, and an apartment building. All of these things would have been challenging for any mainstream urban project. The fact that we dealt with all of that while also creating a Living Building proves what can be done."

CHRISTIAN LAROCCO
Schuchart

REDEFINING THE ADDRESS

The six-story Bullitt Center stands on the site that previously held a one-story wooden commercial building, home to an assortment of tavern businesses that operated between the 1970s and 2010s.

The Bullitt Center team was sensitive to the fact that the most recent occupant of the site — a bar known as C.C. Attle's — was a longtime fixture in the neighborhood and would need ample time to transition to another location. Once that process was complete, the previous structure was carefully deconstructed and virtually all its material was made available for recycle and/or reuse. The lot was now cleared and ready for construction of the Bullitt Center.

Going from one to six stories meant striking a careful balance between the site's carrying capacity with the maximum allowable height and square footage according to zoning requirements. At the outset of the project's design phase, a structure located at 1501 East Madison Street could be no more than 65 feet tall and approximately 50,000 square feet in size. Later, thanks to the City of Seattle's Living Building Pilot Program, the project received permission to extend its overall height by an additional ten feet and another 5,000 square feet. Instead of using the vertical flexibility to add a floor or the overall size flexibility to expand the footprint, the design team added two feet of height to each floor, dramatically increasing the opportunity for daylighting.

WORKING WITH IRREGULARITIES

The five-sided, more-square-than-rectangular configuration of the site, combined with the project's aggressive energy goals, introduced challenges for the designers, engineers, and builders. Not only was the building designed to extend to the far reaches of the lot lines, but its shortest exposure is to the south where most PV-powered structures would typically grab solar rays. For a building to occupy its full lot is not unusual in dense urban neighborhoods, but it is decidedly less common for a zero lot line project to operate on a net zero energy basis. Neighboring structures stand in close proximity on one side of the lot and busy roadways run along two. The Bullitt Center team factored in each site-specific reality as they pondered their design and performance options.

DENIS HAYES
Bullitt Foundation

The building's octagonal footprint introduced complexities to the design-build process, particularly when it came to planning and installing the framework for the rooftop solar array. *Photos: John Stamets*

IMPERATIVE:
HABITAT EXCHANGE

The Living Building Challenge stipulates that projects must set aside an amount of off-site land equal to the size of the development to meet the Habitat Exchange Imperative. Given the ongoing work of the Bullitt Foundation, which devotes substantial resources to conservation efforts as part of its environmental mission, this requirement was easy to satisfy. In fact, Denis Hayes found it a bit irksome in its redundancy. Still, he recognized that the Imperative targeted typical property developers who are not already regularly engaged in the act of saving habitats. So the Bullitt Center completed a transaction to ensure that additional land was protected not just by the Foundation's regular efforts, but courtesy of its headquarters' construction project.

53

There is plenty of space for bikes
to hang around the Bullitt Center.
Photo: Nic Lehoux

54

IMPERATIVE:
CAR FREE LIVING

The topic of automobiles and their relationship to the Bullitt Center was hotly debated from the project's earliest planning charrettes. The building's high walk score and proximity to public transit minimizes occupants' need to drive. But as a commercial office building, doesn't it need to provide at least some on-site parking — if not for tenants then for their visitors? If so, how much is enough? And should the spaces be available to any car or reserved for electric vehicles only?

The team weighed a variety of parking options, seeking a workable solution that fit within the building's small footprint while also adhering to the Car Free Living Imperative. Team members explored the idea of running a ramp down into a small basement parking area, but there was not enough available underground space to accommodate an entire parking level and the associated costs were prohibitive. Then they ran the numbers on offering a handful of plug-in spaces for electric cars, but the potential energy draw involved in recharging even just a few cars threatened to skew the project's net zero operational goal.

Finally, a radical idea came to the table. Alex Steffen, a sustainability writer and strategist participating in the planning process on behalf of Worldchanging, posed a question nobody had considered: "What if the Bullitt Center had no parking at all?" Steffen argued that if the building was intended to stand for 250 years and serve as a symbol of urban sustainability, then it should not be designed around unsustainable present-day modes of transportation. It was a jarring but effective

"When Steffen first proposed the idea of no parking at all, we seriously batted it around, thinking, 'Can we really do a 21st-century office building that doesn't offer parking? Or should we be thinking about this office building as something that suits a later time when cars are not as prominent as they are today?'"

RON ROCHON
The Miller Hull Partnership

"Sometimes, you're prancing around something and the solution is just too radical that it doesn't occur to you. In the case of the parking problem, the best solution was to do nothing at all. It was a high-risk decision, but it was the right one."

DENIS HAYES
Bullitt Foundation

suggestion. Hayes, a longtime proponent of car free cities, swallowed hard and agreed.

The completed building has no on-site car parking whatsoever. Tenants and visitors who bike to the Bullitt Center have access to bicycle storage areas and public transit lines zigzag around the site to deliver people via bus or light rail. For those who need to drive to the building, whether on a daily or occasional basis, several street parking lots are located within a few blocks. Hayes notes that more than a dozen prospective early tenants decided against leasing space principally because they could not imagine coming to work in a building without a parking lot. But organizations committed enough to occupy a Living Building are usually willing to support a car free environment. Sure enough, within two years of completion, the Bullitt Center was fully leased.

55

"As property owners, we evaluate our investments using a triple bottom line. We care about the financial returns on our investments, but we also care about their social and environmental impacts. Having an attractive park adjacent to our building probably enhances the value of the building and certainly improves the experience of our tenants. But it matters to us that the park provides homes for birds and butterflies, that our neighbors play ping pong and chess, and do crosswords, and push baby carriages around a place that had been an empty, desolate, muddy mess."

DENIS HAYES
Bullitt Foundation

"I was always an advocate that the Bullitt Center needed to contribute to the physical development and therefore social development of the neighborhood. So enhancing the little green triangle that was forlorn and inaccessible and is now a gathering point and really a marker for the sub neighborhood – that became an integrated part of the project."

CHRIS ROGERS
Point 32

"There was always an inclination to connect the building to the park; to make it read as one."

MARGARET SPRUG
The Miller Hull Partnership

"The park used to be a patch of lawn that nobody could get to. We wanted to activate it, changing it from a consumptive park to a self-sustaining one."

JONATHAN MORLEY
Berger Partnership

PARK PLACE

McGilvra Place Park occupies the tip of the western-pointing triangle formed by continuing the polygonal Bullitt Center lot lines.

Originally dedicated in 1901, the city-owned half-acre pocket park had fallen into disrepair in recent years.

When Point 32 first acquired the site for the Bullitt Center, McGilvra Place was little more than a traffic median separating East Madison Street and East Pike Street from 15th Avenue. Stately London Plane trees rimmed the park's edges, but a two-foot-high cement perimeter wall made the patchy grass interior feel uninviting.

Hayes and Point 32 saw the park as an opportunity to expand the impact of their project. Improving the aesthetic and environmental profile of the neighboring park would do the same for the building itself while also serving as a gift to the local community. A public-private partnership was formed by the Seattle Department of Parks and Recreation, the Seattle Department of Transportation, the Seattle Parks Foundation, and the Bullitt Foundation, with deep engagement by neighborhood citizens. The group garnered some financial support from the Seattle Parks and Green Spaces Levy Opportunity Fund. In addition, the Foundation sponsored a capital campaign and pledged to maintain the park in future years.

The Berger Partnership was named as the project's landscape design firm, working alongside civil engineers from Springline Design and builders from WS Contractors (all firms that also contributed their expertise to the building). Together, they set out to create a welcoming urban pocket park whose beauty and performance were seamlessly connected to those of its mid-rise neighbor. Holes were knocked in the wall to allow paths through the park, and the grass was all replaced with native vegetation.

The City of Seattle granted permission for 15th Avenue to be closed to through vehicle traffic (although still accessible to emergency vehicles as needed), which encourages pedestrian activity through the park. In addition, scattered benches, a concrete ping pong table, and free wifi — all courtesy of the Bullitt Center — has turned McGilvra Place Park into a local gathering place and contributes to the community-oriented personality of Capitol Hill.

McGilvra Place Park now stands as the world's first Living Park, having received its certification in October 2014.

57

THE WATER PETAL

The Sky's the Limit

58

59

The Water Pearl THE SKY'S THE LIMIT

SUMMARY OF THE LIVING BUILDING CHALLENGE VERSION 2.1 WATER PETAL

Petal Intent

The intent of the Water Petal is to realign how people use water and redefine "waste" in the built environment, so that water is respected as a precious resource. Scarcity of potable water is quickly becoming a serious issue as many countries around the world face severe shortages and compromised water quality. Even regions that have avoided the majority of these problems to date due to a historical presence of abundant fresh water are at risk: the impacts of climate change, highly unsustainable water use patterns, and the continued drawdown of major aquifers portend significant problems ahead.

Petal Imperatives

• Net Zero Water
• Ecological Water Flow

"A typical office building would be designed, built, leased, and sold to an insurance company. Superficially, it might appear to be a financial triumph, because its financial statements ignored all of the external costs that it imposed on its neighbors and society. This nearly universal market pricing failure has created an ecological bubble that dwarfs the trifling dot-com bubble or the 2008 derivatives bubble. Sooner or later, Mother Nature always collects her debts, whether from ancient Babylonians or modern Texans, and she's not above breaking a few knees of those who tried to stiff her. The Bullitt Center has an external impact much like a Douglas fir forest; everyone upstream and downstream is better off because it was built."

DENIS HAYES
Bullitt Foundation

WATER, WATER EVERYWHERE

One might assume it would be relatively easy to build and operate a net zero water structure in a metropolis whose nickname is Rain City. But there is a lot more to the Bullitt Center water story than harvesting the bounty that falls from the sky.

The designers and engineers had to map out complex and inter-related systems of capture, treatment, and reinfiltration that mimicked natural processes as much as possible. If they could not precisely replicate forest hydrology realities, they wanted to get as close as they could.

Before water could be put to use in the building, it had to be collected from the sky. The goal in capturing the rainwater that reaches the site was to mimic predevelopment hydrology. Traditional Seattle structures are rimmed with gutters that divert water onto city streets where it flows untreated toward Lake Union and Puget Sound (picking up pollutants along the way) and robs the underlying aquifer of crucial hydration. At the Bullitt Center, gutters function like the concave leaves of a plant — designed to funnel water so it can stay on-site to serve the structure's systems and eventually replenish the ground beneath.

Planning the building's water infrastructure required as much — if not more — pre-construction coordination among the disciplines as any of the project's other performance areas. Not only did every pipe's route have to be mapped out from rooftop to basement according to its specific function (including the straight, nearly-vertical lines leading from the composting toilets), but each had to stay out of the way of mechanical systems that served common spaces. At the same time, nothing could block the structure's sweeping open interiors or detract from the clean, crisp aesthetics required to qualify it as a Class A office building.

61

LET IT RAIN

The Bullitt Center's hometown has an anecdotal reputation for being the soggiest place in America. But the facts say otherwise.

With average annual rainfall of 38 to 39 inches, Seattle receives less precipitation than Atlanta, Houston, New York, Boston, or Washington DC.[8] Yes, the skies are often grey for eight months of the year, but the ground is not always wet. And climate change is expected to reduce the snowpack in the surrounding mountains, which will alter Seattle's year-round water inventories.

The task for the Bullitt Center team was to harvest every drop of rain that falls directly on the site and put it to work in and for the building. Strategies for rainwater capture were based on three key pieces of data:

- Average annual rainfall volume

- Amount that can be collected within the building footprint

- Average expected daily water demands

8 www.seattle.gov

Photo: Pixabay

Photo: Berger Partnership

"We kept asking ourselves three questions as we sought technical solutions to the building's complex systems – especially water: What's technically feasible, what's economically feasible, and what's feasible from a regulatory standpoint?"

PAUL SCHWER
PAE

"Key to designing the water system was sizing the cistern, and our calculations led us to believe that 56,000 gallons would provide an ample margin of safety. We should be able to have the building fully tenanted – even with a large number of people taking showers after they've biked to work – and still be able to meet all of our water requirements through 100 days without rainfall."

DENIS HAYES
Bullitt Foundation

WET STORAGE

The majority of the rain that falls on the Bullitt Center lands on its ample roof. Beneath the flat, tilted photovoltaic (PV) array, a membrane roof channels water to a series of drain lines that wind their way to the basement. There, water flows through filters into a 56,000 gallon concrete cistern.

The cistern's ideal size was determined by calculating how much water the building would need to sustain its occupants during a 100-day dry spell. Although Seattle has never in recorded history endured more than 51 consecutive days without measurable rain,[9] the building must be prepared to accommodate climatic changes predicted to occur during its intended 250-year lifespan. During typical years, the cistern's levels will rise during winter and spring and fall during summer and autumn. The annual operational goal is to enter the month of June with a full tank.

63

9 www.seattleweatherblog.com

POTABLE WATER: DRINKING IN THE POSSIBILITIES

Through near-Herculean efforts, the Bullitt Center accomplished something no other comparably sized urban commercial structure has ever managed to do: gain regulatory approval to turn harvested on-site rainwater into potable water.

While it was far from the first green building to reach this goal — and wasn't even the first Living Building to do so — the Bullitt Center is the first 52,000 square foot office building serving the general public to convince multiple regulatory agencies that the water that eventually reaches the drinking fountains, sinks, and shower heads is safe for human consumption.

To reach the potable water spigots, rainwater stored in the cistern is pumped through a series of increasingly fine ceramic filters and exposed to ultraviolet light to eliminate contaminants, cysts, bacteria, and even viruses. Finally, to satisfy regulatory requirements, a trace of chlorine is added to the filtered water during its final journey through the pipes. The chlorine is removed from the water using activated charcoal filters when it reaches the taps. (Since chlorine is a Red List material, the team requested and received an exemption for this strategy from the International Living Future Institute, which deemed the larger accomplishment significant enough to justify the work-around. Assuming the Bullitt Center uses 500 gallons of water per day — the full capacity of its day tank — with a chlorine concentration of 1 mg/L, the total chlorine divided daily among all the building's taps would be less than one-third the amount of chlorine bleach recommended for a single load of laundry.)

The Bullitt Center was required to establish itself as an independent Group A water system, which stands separate from but surrounded by the City of Seattle's municipal water system. This led to another interesting question: Because of a voter referendum, the City of Seattle requires Seattle Public Utilities to fluoridate all drinking water, but no one had anticipated the possible creation of a new, independent, site-specific water system within Seattle city limits. It seemed silly to fluoridate the small Bullitt Center water supply that would be used only by adults — not children — and mostly for showers. On behalf of the building, water engineers at Gray & Osborne continued to make that case to regulators, and Seattle finally determined that its fluoridation ordinance does not apply to anything other than its own municipal water supply system. The city acknowledged that it did not have the authority to impose a fluoridation requirement on any other public water system.

From there, Gray & Osborne submitted the building's water system plan to the Washington State Department of Health, which approved it (with some very minor stipulations) in July 2015. The potable water system then underwent its final modifications and became fully operational shortly thereafter. When it did, the Bullitt Center made history. After drawing potable water from municipal lines as it waited for local, state, and even federal regulatory bodies to approve the strategy, it now functions with 100 percent self-sufficiency with regard to water.

"The letter of the Living Building Challenge calls for all water – including potable water – to come from rainwater. But they do offer an out: They say if your local authority will not grant you a permit to do that, you can still be considered a Living Building. We really didn't want to take any of the outs, so Denis and the design team took it upon themselves to go through a Kafkaesque tour through various bureaucracies to get it sorted out."

PAUL SCHWER
PAE

"We got the water system plan together and were ready to submit it to the State Department of Health, but they wouldn't review it until we got a determination on fluoridation. For several weeks, we were stuck in a bureaucratic limbo as the various agencies grappled with our request until we finally got the determination from the Seattle City Attorney, who said the ordinance makes it clear that the Bullitt Center, as a separate water system, shouldn't be required to fluoridate. That's as far as it had to go, so we were done with that issue."

RUSS PORTER
Gray & Osborne

64

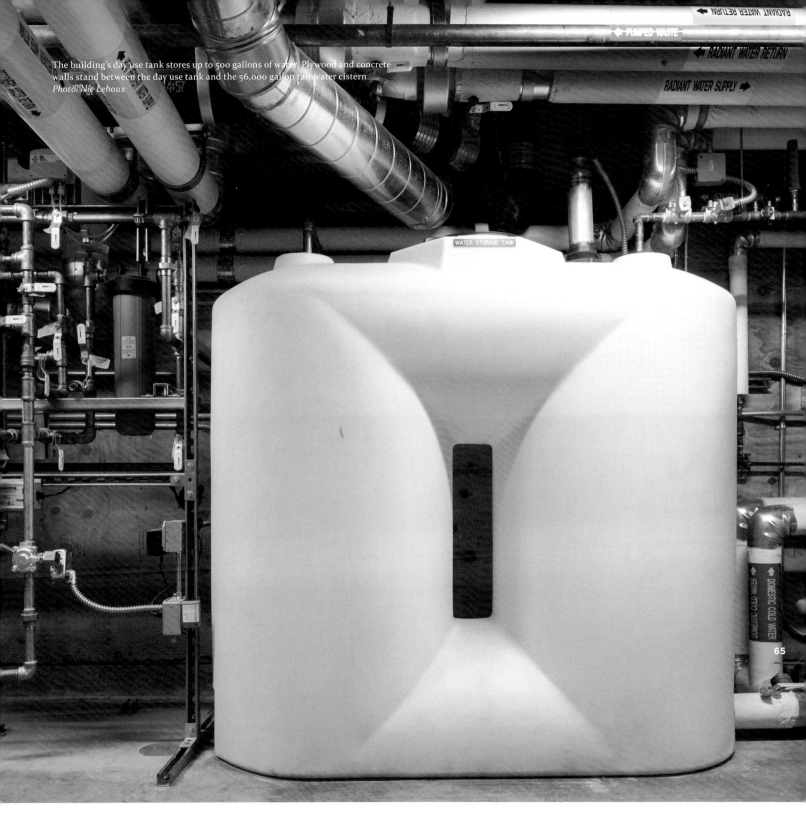

The building's day use tank stores up to 500 gallons of water. Plywood and concrete walls stand between the day use tank and the 56,000 gallon rainwater cistern.
Photo: Nic Lehoux

65

GREYWATER TREATMENT: EXPLORING A VERTICAL SOLUTION

The architects and engineers explored various possible approaches to treating the building's greywater (water that has been used in sinks, drinking fountains, dishwashers, and showers). Of all the ideas that were discussed and eventually discarded, one lingered, primarily because it was the most technically interesting: the stacked greenhouse.

The stacked greenhouse would have stood vertically along four stories of the building's south side. Greywater from the building would have cascaded down a wall of plants, evapotranspiring along the way. It would have produced a dramatic visual effect from any angle, but there were a number of problems with the concept that led to its demise. First, for evaporation to occur within a closed environment, it requires consistent humidity levels and a certain saturation point that would have been difficult to maintain. Second, the water treatment benefits the system offered did not justify the energy needed to pump the greywater to all levels of the greenhouse and heat the plants in the winter. Third, the building was projected to generate too much greywater for the greenhouse's limited square footage to be able to process. Finally, it would have gobbled up valuable rentable space within the building in a section that has views of Mount Rainier and the Olympics. Although the concept was technically intriguing, the downsides outweighed its upsides.

Once the greenhouse idea was officially removed from the plans, the space it would have occupied was redesigned as some of the most delightful offices and conference rooms in the building.

66

"The stacked greenhouse would have been a great way to support a water-independent system, but it would have knocked the energy balance off kilter and would have been too costly to build or manage."

CHRIS ROGERS
Point 32

"Mark Buehrer [from 2020 Engineering] came up with the idea of the stacked greenhouse. It was going to be this big, green, four-story tall greenhouse wrapped in glass where plants would evapotranspire all of the water we needed to get rid of. In the end, it didn't work out, but it was a really cool idea."

BRIAN COURT
The Miller Hull Partnership

"We tried everything we could to make the greenhouse work. Then one day, Conrad Brown at PAE chimed in and said the calculations just weren't penciling out. That was the first time on this project when we said, 'You can't break the laws of physics.'"

MARGARET SPRUG
The Miller Hull Partnership

The Water Petals THE SKY'S THE LIMIT

The greywater infiltration planter and rain garden create a green welcome mat for visitors entering the building from the west. *Photo: Berger Partnership*

68

THE GREENEST BUILDING

"With this greywater system, we're creating ecosystems right on the building and using them for treatment. Not only does it treat the greywater and infiltrate it back into the ground in line with the natural hydrological cycles, but it adds biodiversity in the urban environment."

JUSTIN STENKAMP
PAE

"When we knew we would have a planter on the green roof – under the PV array so it gets next to no rainwater and on the north side so it gets next to no sun – we had to find something that worked well in those conditions. The Equisetum was perfect. It's bullet-proof, it survives anything, and it actually does well when it's contained in tight quarters."

JONATHAN MORLEY
Berger Partnership

THE WINNING GREYWATER APPROACH: NATURE CLEANS UP

Taking what they learned from the many ideas that were explored during the planning phase, the team crafted a greywater treatment solution that combines simplicity, performance, and biomimicry — honoring the goal of replicating the hydrological process of the Douglas fir forest that previously occupied the site.

Just as it purifies rainwater for its occupants' consumption, the Bullitt Center ushers its greywater through an on-site cleaning process before returning it to the earth. Gravity helps water from sinks, drinking fountains, dishwashers, and showers find its way to ground-floor centrifugal filters that remove suspended particles from biodegradable soap and other contaminants that have mixed with the water since it left the potable taps.

The next stop is an adjacent 500-gallon greywater storage tank. From there, dual pumps send doses of greywater throughout the day to a green roof located on the third-floor terrace facing Madison Street. The 800-square-foot constructed wetland, capable of processing approximately 300 gallons of water at a time, is generously stocked with rich soils and porous gravels that break down organic matter and pathogens still present in the water. Hardy horsetail Equisetum, which thrives in such nutrient-rich conditions, consumes and evapotranspires most of the water while lending a decorative touch to the green roof. After the greywater has been recirculated through the wetlands several times (a function that occurs automatically but can be managed manually), any overflow drips through an irrigation system leading from the green roof to the street level, where it reaches the bioswales that line the public entrance on the west side of the building.

REINFILTRATION: RETURNING THE FAVOR

Of the estimated 400 gallons of water that can flow through the Bullitt Center during an average day of full occupancy (shy of the day tank's full capacity of 500 gallons), approximately 5 percent is consumed by the occupants. The resulting greywater evapotranspires via the wetland plants on the green roof.

The balance of the treated greywater from the constructed wetlands trickles down a vertical pipe to the ground level for irrigation use, where it evapotranspires or infiltrates into the native landscape.(During dryer summer months, nearly 100 percent of the water evapotranspires, so very little treated greywater reaches this stage of the treatment cycle.) This final cleaning step ensures that the water ultimately returned to the aquifer is as clean — if not cleaner — than what falls from the sky onto the building. It also adheres to the Living Building Challenge requirement that no water leaves a site via municipal sewer lines.

Stormwater infiltration strategies line the 15th Avenue pedestrian walkway between McGilvra Place Park and the public entrance to the building. The first, planted with red twig dogwood, takes greywater from the building and releases it below the surface to a series of 30-foot drain wells deep enough to reach the underground sand layers. Water that makes it this far through the Bullitt Center journeys down one last rocky path before finally percolating into the sand and soil beneath. A second planter serves as a wetland to cleanse and delay any surface water from the sidewalks and roof areas on the west side of the building. Both the rooftop and ground level wetlands are planted with horsetail Equisetum for visual consistency.

Because the bioswales sit just beyond the Bullitt Center's property line on a public thoroughfare, and because they function as a miniaturized water treatment facility, the City of Seattle and other regulating agencies had to get involved in the permitting process. After all, typical buildings send all wastewater directly to the sewer without asking for any departure from standard permitting procedures. Eventually, the city deferred to the State Department of Health, which granted special permission once the engineers could prove that all treated greywater passing through the building would get biologically processed to remove contaminants through the green roof before being infiltrated via the bioswales. Key to the process was convincing regulators that no water that finds its way to the 15th Avenue infiltration gallery is a hazard to the public.

Stormwater and runoff that hits the sidewalk in the vicinity of the infiltration gallery has to be kept separate. Surface water is channeled into a separate runnel that bypasses the bioswales and flows into a rain garden on the south side of the building. Also planted with horsetail Equisetum, the rain garden is aesthetically and functionally expressive.

Photo: Berger Partnership

"One big hiccup with the greywater drain field area was that it stood in the public right of way, which triggered a city and state review. It's highly treated greywater and isn't a hazard, but it's still categorized as greywater, which is categorized as wastewater."

MARK BUEHRER
2020 Engineering

"All these little solutions ... it's only once you realize the puzzle that's trying to be solved when you start to really appreciate it."

JONATHAN MORLEY
Berger Partnership

"We had to figure out how to get rid of greywater without putting it in a pipe. Evaporate it? Absorb it? Infiltrate it? We explored each of those options to the fullest extent and realized that we could clean the water within the property line, but we couldn't get rid of it within that line. That's how the infiltration wells in the right of way came about. We decided it was worth hurdling the municipality."

RACHAEL MEYER
Berger Partnership

71

"It's not an exaggeration to say that much of the building was designed around the composting toilets. The size of the space needed in the basement for the composting units, for example, was critical. In addition to wanting to place the restrooms where there was the least daylight, the position of the composters below drove where the restrooms would go, how the toilets had to be placed, and the distribution of the piping."

MARK BUEHRER
2020 Engineering

"From a mechanical engineering standpoint, composting requires a new way to think about commissioning systems. In a typical mechanical system, you come in and commission it and you're done. But with a composting system, it's living so it takes time to mature. A composting system won't hit its operational efficiency peak for one to two years after it's up and running."

JUSTIN STENKAMP
PAE

NOTHING IS WASTED

The third and arguably most impressive aspect of the water treatment strategy has to do with human waste. The Bullitt Center is hardly the first structure to have tackled independent on-site blackwater treatment. However, it is by far the largest, tallest structure and the only Class A office building to have taken on such a formidable task within the framework of the Living Building Challenge.

The architects and engineers first considered the most widely implemented green building solution for wastewater treatment: a living machine. (Developed by biologist and ecological designer John Todd, the living machine is a computer-controlled bioremediation system that mimics the function of a tidal wetland to treat and/or reuse wastewater.) But they quickly decided against that option after calculating the amount of real estate and energy required to operate a living machine in a 52,000 square foot building with tight perimeter constraints and an even tighter energy budget.

Next on the agenda was a composting system. The minimal environmental impact of composting complemented the project's larger sustainability mission, but there were serious concerns about whether it was realistic within a six-story structure. Although the engineers ran the numbers and confirmed that it was physically possible in the Bullitt Center, questions remained

about whether it was prudent to embrace such a radical idea for such a fundamental and outward-facing component of the building. It would also demand that the engineers design a system that had never been tested on this scale. Finally, it was important to weigh how potential tenants would respond to the idea of composting toilets in their high-end commercial office building.

The fact that a composting system would echo the building's Living theme ultimately helped tip the scales in favor of a composting strategy. But it was an enormous decision to make, as it affected virtually every aspect of the overall layout and involved significant integration of other systems. The team was also aware that most people assume a composting toilet is more like an outhouse than a fully functioning bathroom fixture; they had to replicate the modern-day "user experience" as much as possible for the strategy to be deemed successful.

Photo: Nic Lehoux

"There was some concern that using a composting system would raise the bar for entry for other Living Building projects. But after being in the building and interpreting it for visitors, I can report that it's really the most visible thing we take to the public. In terms of the story of the final building, it's essential. This building is a conversation starter, and the composting toilets are a big part of that."

ROB PEÑA
Integrated Design Lab

"You get into some really interesting research when you're trying to calculate how much urine is produced by a person between 8:00 a.m. and 5:00 p.m."

MARK BUEHRER
2020 Engineering

"Standard flushing toilets are a huge source of biological contamination, even in homes where toilets commonly have lids. In public toilets, it can pose a genuine hazard. Our foaming toilets don't create all those aerosols."

DENIS HAYES
Bullitt Foundation

73

The Water Petal: THE SKY'S THE LIMIT

FLUSHLESS SUCCESS

The fire code allows the Bullitt Center to accommodate up to 350 people. The building is expected to house an average density of approximately 250 workers at full occupancy, and additional people will come and go to visit tenants and tour the site.

Designing a composting toilet strategy required making the types of calculations few of the team members had previously researched: How many toilets would be needed? How many times would each fixture be used each day? What volume of liquid and solid waste would enter the system on a daily, weekly, monthly, yearly basis? At what times of day would the system be in highest demand? How much water would be needed to flush each toilet? How much energy would be required to power ventilation?

The resulting data helped determine the ideal system design. Thirty-two foam-flush, waterless Phoenix Toilets manufactured in Whitefish, Montana are distributed among the building's six floors. An automatic sensor at each fixture detects the presence of a new user. Before each use, the funnel-shaped toilet basin is quickly coated with a biodegradable foam that requires approximately three ounces of water per application (depending on the length of the visit) and helps eliminate friction within the pipe as material passes through. Waste then travels down a nearly vertical pipe to the basement, where it reaches one of ten Phoenix Composters, each 84" x 40" x 61" in size. The waste mixes with wood chips stored inside the composting units and the contents are "stirred" regularly to encourage an aerobic decomposition process. As biosolids decompose, the particles shrink and gradually filter down to the lower levels of the composters. After approximately 18 months, the bottom layer of the unit's contents is removed and given to a local company that combines the biosolids with sawdust and packages it as GroCo compost.

Excess liquids from the composters are diverted into a separate set of leachate storage tanks also located on the building's ground floor. The stabilized leachate is taken in monthly batches to the King County Liquid Waste facility in nearby Carnation, Washington, where it is combined with other compostable materials generated by the county's waste treatment facility.

The Bullitt Center discharges zero wastewater into the municipal sewer system.

Airflow plays an important role in the science and elegance of the composting system. Not only is oxygen required to ensure the solid waste's aerobic decomposition within the holding units (and prevent sepsis within the pile), but managing odor at every step of the process is a critical concern. To keep air circulating throughout the system, each restroom is negatively pressurized. Air is drawn gently through slats in the bathroom doors and down through the toilets all the way to the ground-level composters. Since there can be no barriers preventing gravity to carry waste material straight from the Bullitt Center toilet bowls to the composting units, there are no traps beneath the individual fixtures the way there are in standard toilets. While this makes it difficult — and quite unpleasant — to retrieve any accidentally dropped valuables, it eliminates the possibility of smells or gases seeping upwards from the pipes back into the restrooms.

A serious public health issue in most commercial restrooms is the explosive distribution of bacteria when toilets are flushed with 1.5 to 4 gallons of water. Public toilets generally don't have lids, and lids are rarely used even when present. Often the flush is automatic. With the Bullitt Center's foam-flush, however, gravity carries the fecal material to the basement. And the constant negative air pressure ensures that pathogens aren't expelled into the atmosphere.

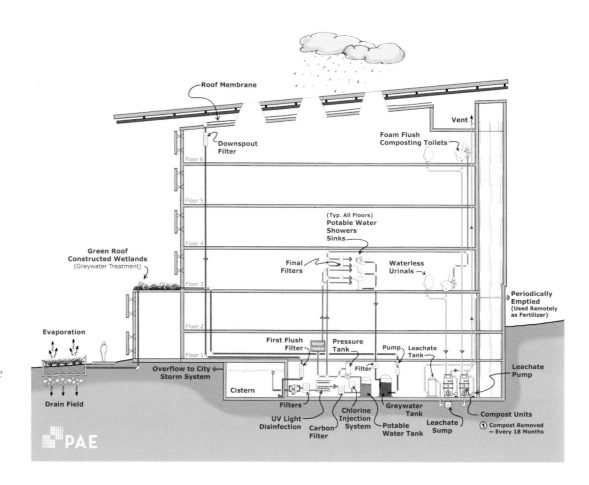

> *"People always assume composting toilets will be stinky. But there's actually less odor in a composting toilet bathroom because the odors generated in the bowl go straight down to the basement and through the pile of wood chips, then are drawn back up through a stack to the roof of the building."*

MARK BUEHRER
2020 Engineering

> *"Our composting process returns the nutrients back to the soil, sequesters the carbon, and does all the good things we want."*

DENIS HAYES
Bullitt Foundation

IMPERATIVE:
ECOLOGICAL WATER FLOW

The Bullitt Center registered under Version 2.0 of the Living Building Challenge, which was the final iteration of the standard that included the Ecological Water Flow Imperative as a stand-alone requirement. (As of Version 3.0, released in May 2014, the concept of ecological water flow is woven into the single Water Petal Imperative: Net Positive Water.) The purpose of the Imperative is to mimic natural downstream hydrological patterns within the built environment without sending excess runoff into a combined municipal sewer system.

To meet this requirement, the team looked at what water flow patterns existed when the Bullitt Center site was an old-growth

forest. Under those conditions, the team calculated, approximately 40 to 50 percent of the water would have evaporated from the trees before it ever reached the ground. The rest of the water would have migrated downhill in streams and through the soil.

Given its final water capture and treatment infrastructure, the Bullitt Center patterns are comparable to those of its forested predecessor: Tenants of the building consume a significant amount; much of the greywater evaporates from the building's green roof; and it actively reinfiltrates an amount proportional to what once reached the forest floor.

A TANGLED PATH TO REGULATORY APPROVAL

Seeking and gaining regulatory approval for the complex — and in some aspects unique — Bullitt Center water strategies proved to be one of the most difficult tasks throughout the project's entire design and construction process.

Each tier of the system is overseen by multiple agencies, depending on the water's source, use, location, and destination, so documenting and permitting the infrastructure became a complicated exercise. City, county, and state regulators weighed in on various water-related concerns, with certain issues rising as high as the federal level.

Perhaps the most challenging aspect of all was getting permission to flow filtered, purified rainwater through the building's interior taps. First, the City of Seattle said no. Then King County said no. Then the State Department of Health said no. All classified the building's treated rainwater as wastewater, deeming it unsafe for human consumption and a potential risk to the public water supply. The engineers came back with data showing that the water that reached Bullitt Center fountains, sinks, and shower heads would be cleaner than the drinking water available to the vast majority of human beings around the globe. But nothing would sway the regulators. There was only one thing that would change their minds: chlorine. They stipulated that if the Bullitt Center wanted its tenants to be able to drink rainwater, a small amount of chlorine would have to be added. This, they argued, would form a final protective barrier between pathogens and the public. But chlorine is a Red List material and is not allowed in a Living Building. If the building's water system contained it, it could threaten the project's certification chances.

So Denis Hayes decided to elevate the discussion, contacting the head of the water program at the U.S. Environmental Protection Agency (EPA). Hayes reasoned that state-of-the-art technology was in place to ensure that the treated water would be safe without chlorine — safer, in fact, than most of what is consumed anywhere in the world. Hayes's request was denied. Rather than receive the EPA's blessing, he was told that the Agency had no flexibility under the clear language of the federal Safe Drinking Water Act (a law that, ironically, Hayes had lobbied for in his youth). Unless he launched a campaign to amend the federal law — not a wise move for an environmentalist facing an anti-environmental Congress — he would have to abide by that law.

Moreover, then-EPA Administrator Lisa P. Jackson argued persuasively that the chlorine provision of the law was actually good public policy. There have been dozens of documented cases of water-borne illness in private residences that had ultra-clean water supplies from wells but where bacteria had entered the plumbing through the "back door," via faucets and shower heads, and contaminated the water right in the pipes. By adding trace amounts of chlorine to its already-clean water, the Bullitt Center would protect its tenants from such problems.

Unico engineers perform daily checks on the ten composters located in the building, adding wood chips to the mix when needed.

Photo: Nic Lehoux

ENGINEERS IN THE HOUSE

Overseeing building performance is part of Unico Properties' responsibilities as property manager at the Bullitt Center. On-site engineer Corey Reilly keeps a close eye on all systems on a day-to-day basis, calling on Unico's Seattle-area engineering team as needed to address larger issues. Together, they are charged with optimizing performance throughout the building.

On the water side, Reilly ensures that all capture, treatment, landscaping, and reinfiltration systems are operating as they should. Among his duties is checking the toilets and composters daily to confirm that they are clean and functional. On most days, Reilly dons a Tyvek® suit and applies wood chips to the biosolids inside the composters to spur the decomposition process.

"Corey is a fantastic engineer. He has fully embraced the brilliance of Living Buildings and how they're capable of transforming the built environment, so he's a perfect fit for the Bullitt Center."

BRETT PHILLIPS
Unico Properties

Photo: Berger Partnership

"Don't just go to the regulators after designs are all done and ask for approval. Some officials felt that we had been a little presumptuous, a little arrogant, to have designed and built a novel water collection and purification system and just assumed the regulators would go along. Our actual sin was not arrogance but innocence. We thought we were holding ourselves to incredibly high standards, but the regulators found things that were wrong with our systems. They were, for the most part, deeply experienced professionals who were intrigued by what we were trying to accomplish, and they added genuine value to the project. I'm confident they would have been collegial partners if we had asked them from the start to help us solve our problems."

DENIS HAYES
Bullitt Foundation

WATER: LESSONS LEARNED

There was no precedent for the types of systems that were designed and engineered for the Bullitt Center. For virtually every performance area, the team had to develop first-of-their-kind strategies using the distinct goals and specifications of this one project. Now that the building is complete and operational, the architects, engineers, and owner can look back and evaluate what they might do differently if they had the chance.

With regard to water, key lessons learned include:

INVOLVE THE REGULATORS EARLY ON. Local and state agencies were brought in to assess water systems after they were designed. Hayes, for one, believes that the permitting process would have gone more smoothly had the regulators been consulted in detail from the start — even been invited to join the integrated design team for water. Doing so would have saved significant time, trouble, and money.

ASK BEFORE SPECIFYING. Point 32, Schuchart, and Miller Hull conducted significant research and identified an inert, Red List-compliant rooftop membrane that would prevent chemicals from leaching into the rainwater before it traveled to the cistern for storage. Still, the state required a different coating that met additional standards.

CONSIDER THE SCALE. The Bullitt Center proves that water independence for a 52,000 square foot building is, indeed, feasible. However, the cost and technical effort required to achieve this goal at the building scale further demonstrates that the ecodistrict scale is often more cost-effective.

THE ENERGY PETAL

A Higher Power

81

The Energy Petal: **A HIGHER POWER**

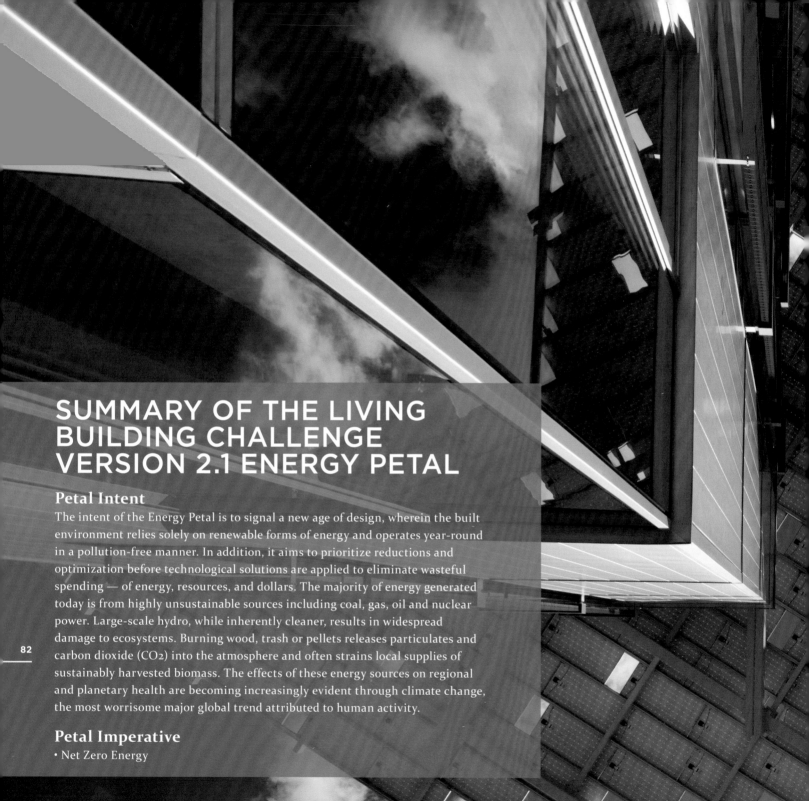

SUMMARY OF THE LIVING BUILDING CHALLENGE VERSION 2.1 ENERGY PETAL

Petal Intent

The intent of the Energy Petal is to signal a new age of design, wherein the built environment relies solely on renewable forms of energy and operates year-round in a pollution-free manner. In addition, it aims to prioritize reductions and optimization before technological solutions are applied to eliminate wasteful spending — of energy, resources, and dollars. The majority of energy generated today is from highly unsustainable sources including coal, gas, oil and nuclear power. Large-scale hydro, while inherently cleaner, results in widespread damage to ecosystems. Burning wood, trash or pellets releases particulates and carbon dioxide (CO_2) into the atmosphere and often strains local supplies of sustainably harvested biomass. The effects of these energy sources on regional and planetary health are becoming increasingly evident through climate change, the most worrisome major global trend attributed to human activity.

Petal Imperative

• Net Zero Energy

Photo: Nic Lehoux

"*There are two things that are always true in nature: one is that 99.9 percent of life gets its energy from the sun either directly or indirectly, and the second is that nature ruthlessly roots out inefficiency. In this building, we have tried to emulate both of those things.*"

DENIS HAYES
Bullitt Foundation

THE CLARITY OF HAYES

Denis Hayes has devoted much of his adult life to promoting the virtues of solar energy. So when it came time to design the Bullitt Center's energy strategies, it was obvious to everyone involved that the building would need to stand as a bold, dramatic demonstration piece; proof that nature's most abundant currency is powerful enough to sustain the human-built environment.

If photosynthesis can harness enough energy to power every living thing on earth while using a trivial fraction of incident sunshine, photovoltaic (PV) panels should similarly be able to harness enough to power the built environment.

Creating a six-story structure that relies fully on sunbeams in cloudy Seattle was the one project goal that was never up for compromise. Hayes knew it, Miller Hull knew it, PAE knew it, and Schuchart knew it. The only question at the start of the design phase was how to make it happen.

83

NET ZERO ENERGY AS DESIGN DRIVER

The energy budget of a net zero energy building hinges on two basic requirements: maximizing supply and minimizing demand. For this 52,000 square foot net zero commercial Living Building, though, penciling out the energy equation was a massive undertaking that affected virtually every other aspect of the structure's design. Nowhere in the world had such operational efficiency been attempted in a single building, so it was up to the Bullitt Center team — and additional source experts brought in to help — to chart this new territory.

PAE began by running energy models asking how much electricity could be generated by the most efficient commercial panels covering the entire gross surface area of the PV site (calculated as approximately 14,000 square feet) given Seattle's annualized daylight averages. The answer: about 250,000 kilowatt hours in an average year. The next step was figuring out how to operate within that fixed solar energy budget — without exceeding the physical boundaries of an extremely tight urban lot and while also meeting every other Living Building Challenge performance requirement.

Even PAE's Paul Schwer admits to moments of doubt early on. He was fairly confident that a four- or perhaps even a five-story solar-powered building could be done, but he worried about the feasibility of stretching as high as six floors with nothing but the sun keeping the electricity flowing. Still, he and his associates worked closely with Miller Hull on the delicate back-and-forth between design and engineering until viable options emerged.

Along the way, they received valuable input from the growing roster of individuals who offered their professional expertise to the project. Among them was Steven Strong of Solar Design Associates, a longtime friend of Hayes and an internationally recognized authority on renewable energy systems, who consulted on the project as energy strategies took shape. Strong worked side by side with the engineers and architects as the team weighed the key variables that were outside the team's control (such as climate and sunlight) as well as those that were changeable (such as daylighting strategies, occupant use patterns, plug loads, etcetera). Those data points were then factored into calculations surrounding the single most critical number related to the project's energy strategy: its EUI.

Photo: Nic Lehoux

"We all knew that the core challenge was all about reducing demand. And the Bullitt Center was going to have to go beyond anything that had previously been achieved in terms of efficiency. It would have to use about half the energy as the best examples up to that point in commercial buildings – including projects I'd worked on."

STEVEN STRONG
Solar Design Associates

"One thread running through the whole process was coupling the Net Zero Energy Imperative with replicability and financial responsibility – it was really clarifying and made it pretty easy to see which ideas we needed to hold onto and what we needed to let go of."

RON ROCHON
The Miller Hull Partnership

"I must admit I was skeptical. After Denis interviewed us for the job, I ran some quick numbers on using solar for a six-story building but it required an EUI that was so low and had never been accomplished. I thought we were biting off a little bit more than we could chew, and assumed we would end up with four or five floors."

PAUL SCHWER
PAE

The Energy Petal: A HIGHER POWER

FINDING THE EUI SWEET SPOT

A building's energy use intensity — or EUI — is determined by the energy it uses per year divided by its gross square footage.

The EUI of a building is a similar metric to the MPG of a car (although a lower EUI is better for a building, while a higher MPG is better for a car). When the Bullitt Center was being designed in 2010-2011, the average EUI of all Seattle office buildings was approximately 92. Even the sub-set of local commercial structures that were built to LEED Platinum standards and designed to satisfy Seattle's strict energy code operated at an average EUI of between 34 and 50.

In order to achieve net zero energy — to consume no more energy than was produced by the most efficient solar panels covering the greatest possible area — the Bullitt Center had

to achieve an EUI of 16. It was an intimidating goal, but one that Hayes made clear was non-negotiable. The team rose to the challenge with enthusiasm, knowing that if they succeeded they would be setting a new milestone. There were three broad categories of concern: designing and constructing the building to minimize the energy necessary to keep its occupants comfortable; choosing the most efficient mechanical systems to operate the building; and persuading tenants to minimize "plug loads" by using very efficient computers, printers, copiers, task lamps, etcetera and by using this equipment in an efficient manner.

"Engineers talk a lot about EUI because it's a number you can apply to all of a building. A subtlety in designing a net zero energy building is that the EUI isn't as important as the absolute amount of energy it will have access to once you decide how much PV to put on. We ended up having this number in our head that was very specific to this building. It was roughly 240,000 kilowatt hours per year. That became our budget."

PAUL SCHWER, PAE

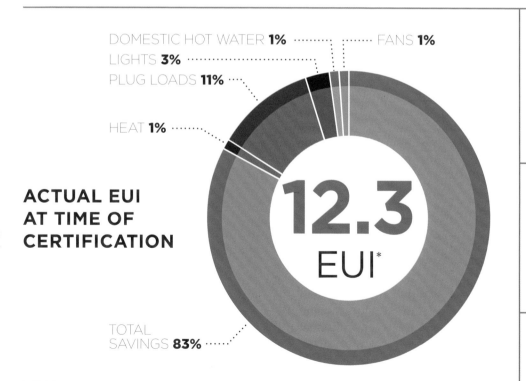

DOMESTIC HOT WATER **1%**
LIGHTS **3%**
PLUG LOADS **11%**
HEAT **1%**
FANS **1%**

ACTUAL EUI AT TIME OF CERTIFICATION

12.3 EUI*

TOTAL SAVINGS **83%**

74.2%
SAVINGS FROM BASELINE

47.7
KBTU/SF/YEAR BASELINE EUI**

* Actual EUI at the time of certification

** ASHRAE 90.1 – 2007, Medium Office category, all climates

ENERGY USE INTENSITY (EUI)

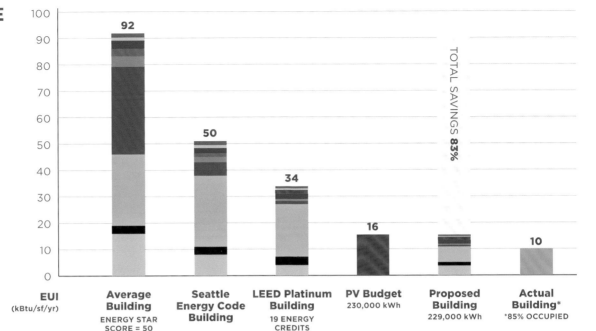

Legend:
- DOM. HOT WATER
- ELEVATOR
- VENT FANS
- PUMPS & AUX
- SPACE COOLING
- SPACE HEATING
- PLUG LOADS
- IT SERVER
- LIGHTS

EUI (kBtu/sf/yr)

Building	EUI
Average Building — ENERGY STAR SCORE = 50	92
Seattle Energy Code Building	50
LEED Platinum Building — 19 ENERGY CREDITS	34
PV Budget — 230,000 kWh	16
Proposed Building — 229,000 kWh	16
Actual Building* — *85% OCCUPIED	10

TOTAL SAVINGS **83%**

"Plug loads were the big unknown. We did a substantial amount of research into the most efficient office equipment we could find. Making the assumption that we could find a way to persuade all tenants to dramatically reduce their plug loads by using super-efficient devices allowed us to drive the EUI down into the neighborhood of 16. We knew we could design and build a super-efficient building, but ultimately it would be up to the landlord to incentivize the very low plug loads and the tenants to achieve them."

JIM HANFORD, The Miller Hull Partnership

"When we started, we thought the most aggressive target we could hit was around 22 or 23. That was about as efficient as we thought we could design any building. So we started asking how much PV we would need to get there. But we couldn't get enough panels on the roof to reach that EUI. That's when we started doing the calculations the other way – seeing what EUI we would need to get to, given the amount of PV we could put on the building."

PAUL SCHWER, PAE

"Designing the building to meet the 16 EUI goal meant planning for the worst case as far as occupant energy use so that Denis had every option when he was leasing the building. We assumed every floor would be fully occupied and every work station would use a heavy load. In the end, we couldn't make a six-story net zero energy building pencil out in Seattle without counting on tenants using highly efficient equipment and modifying their behavior to accommodate the energy mission."

BRIAN COURT, The Miller Hull Partnership

"The amount of sunlight available in Seattle is modest, but the climate is relatively forgiving. So that was the offsetting benefit that made the project possible. If we had that small amount of sun in a more demanding climate, net zero energy would have been more of a challenge."

STEVEN STRONG, Solar Design Associates

The Energy Petal: **A HIGHER POWER**

"If this building weren't on an urban home-plate-shaped site and we weren't trying to achieve all of the Living Building Challenge goals, it would have taken on a much different form."

BRIAN COURT
The Miller Hull Partnership

FORM ENABLES FUNCTION

Miller Hull played with an "alphabet soup" of shapes searching for the form that would best support the building's energy performance goals while also achieving the Living Building Challenge Imperative (from the Health Petal) requiring that each permanent desk be within 30 feet of an operable window.

Each design was digitally modeled to see how and where natural light flowed through interior spaces during different times of day and through all four seasons. It seemed logical to create a central atrium to minimize the distance daylight had to travel, so two of the three final designs featured open cores.

Three conceptual building shapes were the most thoroughly vetted:

THE O

A circular scheme with a courtyard in the center emerged from the assumption that such a shape would maximize daylighting opportunities. But given the configuration of the site, the height of the structure, and the narrowness of the atrium, not enough sunlight would reach into the lower floors to achieve the daylighting needs. This was especially true in winter, when the sun was low on the horizon, cloud cover was thickest, and daylighting needs were greatest. In addition, the open core would lead to heat loss that would skew energy performance.

THE U

This building form remained on the table longer than the O. Unlike the doughnut shape, the U was open at the southeast side, which would allow unobstructed daylight to reach all six stories. However, it robbed the structure of useable office space and required more skin to cover the exterior walls that faced the atrium. Ultimately, both atrium schemes were abandoned for cost and performance reasons.

THE T

The Bullitt Center's final shape (whose roofline extends outward from the vertical building to form a T when the structure is viewed from the ground) emerged out of a combination of daylighting analysis, energy performance calculations, and cost considerations. By putting all shared functions — lavatories, conference rooms, and kitchens — in the core of the building, all the permanent desks could be kept within 30 feet of a window around the perimeter.

Photo: Brent Smith

"I assumed the atrium design was going to win out, but it was an inward-facing solution that was all about the space inside and would have been a bit lifeless from the exterior. With our final design, we turned the building inside out. It's so much better, but I don't think we could have gotten there if we hadn't had all the other performance pressures placed on us."

MARGARET SPRUG
The Miller Hull Partnership

"I chose the site because it had so many desirable features: guaranteed access to sunlight; convenience to multiple modes of public transit; location in a neighborhood of 'cultural creatives.' What I didn't appreciate were the formidable design challenges that would be posed by its awkward pentagonal shape. If I were to develop another Living Building in Seattle, I would try to find a long, narrow lot stretching from east to west."

DENIS HAYES
Bullitt Foundation

89

"We had to do everything we could to maximize daylight – not just the quantity but the quality of it. The daylighting was probably the most scrutinized part of the project from our side."

BRIAN COURT
The Miller Hull Partnership

90

Photo: The Miller Hull Partnership

IN THE LIGHT OF DAY

One of the project's critical goals was to eliminate the need for artificial general
lighting during daytime hours. As the building design began to form, Rob Peña and
the Integrated Design Lab (IDL) worked closely with PAE and Miller Hull to tighten the
daylighting strategies. With electric lighting gobbling up approximately 25 percent of the
preliminary building-wide energy budget, the team sought ways to bring as many rays
of natural light into the space as possible. The more daylight, the less artificial light.

The process involved many rounds of backs-and-forths among
the various disciplines. Similar to what occurred during the
project's cost estimating phase, daylighting ideas were vetted for
their usability, then either rejected outright or reworked. Each
iteration sought to maximize light in ways that were economically
feasible and allowable by the Living Building Challenge.

Ultimately, the group landed on a daylighting solution
that hinged on an unconventional framing solution
involving an upturned beam at the perimeter, which frees
up eight inches of additional unobstructed glazing.

After studying the models and experimenting with various
possible design approaches, the team determined that the
best way to incorporate the upturned beam idea and achieve
the project's daylighting goals was to increase the height of
the window head above the floor. The only way to do this was
to utilize the city's Living Building Pilot Program ordinance
that allowed for an additional ten feet of building height,
which increased floor-to-floor heights from 10'-6" to 13'-10".

When the City of Seattle allowed a departure from maximum
allowable height, which extended the overall building height

from 65 feet to 75 feet, it solidified the daylighting plan.
(This was just one of the many allowances included in the
Living Building Pilot Program that meant that the project
could be built to code, albeit a newly modified one. For more
information on the Living Building Pilot Program, see page 41.)

Other developers not striving for net zero energy might
use an extra ten feet of height to add another story. At the
Bullitt Center, it was used to increase the height of each of
the six stories. As a result, daylight extends another three
to four feet into each level's interior space reaching all the
way to the structure's core elements (restrooms, elevator
shaft, etcetera) that use artificial lighting or none at all.

"We had lighting designers, architects, and engineers
 trying to figure out a way to get light deeper into the
 space, and that's where we came up with the upturned
 beam. Raising the floor-to-floor to the equivalent height
 of an upturned beam would have been very expensive
 since it would require buying that equivalent amount of
 building skin on every floor. We did it a different way."

PAUL SCHWER, PAE

"Lots of people don't like fluorescents, and other people don't like LEDs or incandescents, but no one doesn't like sunlight. There are very few areas of this building where artificial lights automatically go on. You have to make a formal effort to do it. Most spaces are so naturally bright that it doesn't occur to people to turn on a light."

DENIS HAYES
Bullitt Foundation

"The building is delightfully lit. We're in buildings all the time that are lit up like operating rooms and if you were in a place like that for eight or ten hours a day, you might come to the Bullitt Center and think it's a cave. But if you spend just a small amount of time and acclimate, it's delightful."

STEVEN STRONG
Solar Design Associates

WINDOWS OF OPPORTUNITY

Deciding on how to organize the building's windows in the context of the façade design was critical to the daylighting scheme. Miller Hull's Jim Hanford and IDL's Chris Meek modeled alternatives in search of the best solution capable of marrying performance requirements, structural necessities, aesthetic considerations, and budgetary realities.

Miller Hull pushed hard on the glass. The firm is known for relying heavily on glazing to maximize natural light in all of its Pacific Northwest projects, so the designers wanted to push the Bullitt Center glazing percentage as high as possible. The architects engaged in a constructive debate with PAE, advocating for as much as 50 percent glazing while the engineers suggested closer to 30 percent. With each new idea, PAE and IDL ran digital models to test its daylighting and

thermal effects while Schuchart penciled out how it might affect the costs of the curtain wall and the building envelope.

When all the pieces aligned, the window strategy was finalized. On average, the overall building is 40 percent glazed while the main daylighting façades are 60 percent glazed. The triple-pane, argon-filled, low-E glass windows are configured in vertical strips, which allows unfettered light to enter the building and bathe the interiors.

Photo: Nic Lehoux

1501

93

The Energy Petal: A HIGHER POWER

"*Some young employees view hjgh-powered computers the way my generation used to view high-powered cars. Few Ferrari owners get their cars into the red zone, but they like having all that untapped power under the hood. Meanwhile, they get eight miles per gallon. Similarly, some people want to have the fastest, most powerful computers on the market, even though their work could be performed just as well on a machine that uses far less energy.*"

DENIS HAYES
Bullitt Foundation

Photo: Nic Lehoux

94

"*The design of this building changed how I run my business. We used to run about 260 watts at every work station, and now it's down to about 50. I have the same screen area and get the same performance out of my equipment. It's just that we select those things much more carefully now. When you're held to it, it really makes a difference.*"

PAUL SCHWER
PAE

"*Denis knew, because of his background in renewables, that the solar input and its harvest would be the critical determinant as to whether this project would be viable or not. We had a finite amount of roof area. My job was to make sure it produced just as much electricity as possible.*"

STEVEN STRONG
Solar Design Associates

CARRYING THE OCCUPANT LOAD

Occupant behavior is very important to any building's energy consumption. In a traditional residential structure, a family can lower its power bill by making minor adjustments to their habits.

In a typical commercial office building, however, owners have very little control over tenants' usage patterns. Things would need to be different at the Bullitt Center. Even though tenants would be required to sign low-use commitments as part of the lease, the architects and engineers knew that occupants held more than half of the energy cards. The meticulously calculated and fiercely protected energy budget could be thrown off by a single tenant's bank of inefficient computers. Still, it was up to the team to create a Class A office building. Prospective tenants need to feel confident that they can rent Bullitt Center offices without having to compromise their business practices.

Even PAE's Paul Schwer — the project's chief mechanical engineer — had concerns about signing the usage agreement

prior to opening his firm's Seattle offices inside the Bullitt Center. Theoretically, he fully supported the idea of asking tenants to participate in energy efficiency. But he wondered whether PAE, a collection of engineers using powerful computers, could actually meet the goals. He measured PAE's energy use per employee in its Portland office and discovered vastly higher numbers than what would be acceptable at the Bullitt Center. The process led to dramatic changes across the firm. He discovered that by carefully matching computers, printers, and other equipment to the actual requirements of a job, the firm could reduce its energy use by a staggering 82 percent. Schwer rapidly implemented the same changes in all its offices and now the same levels of efficiency required by the Bullitt Center for PAE's Seattle operation are realized in every location.

THE SOUTH ARRAY THAT ALMOST WAS

On their way to designing a successful solar strategy for the Bullitt Center, team members considered a number of creative ideas. Many were quickly set aside when they were unable to balance the equation between generation and usage in a fully occupied commercial building. However, one possible approach elicited strong support from some members of the team: a proposed south-facing vertical wall composed of 222 solar modules, cantilevered out to cover the top four stories of the building.

Now affectionately referred to as the "mud flap" or, less affectionately, as the "combover," the south array was intended to supplement the power generated by the rooftop solar panels. It was still being seriously considered as late as the construction document phase. Proponents argued that the proposed south array would tilt the energy scale in a slightly more comfortable direction; detractors contended the small amount of supplemental energy it would contribute could never justify the expected seven-figure price tag that would accompany the extra panels and the framework to hold them safely in place.

The south array debate swirled around these key points:

THE PROS

- Creates a bold architectural statement

- Offers visible demonstration of renewable energy

- Harvests an additional 38,500 kilowatt hours of electricity per year, improving the odds of being net energy positive

THE CONS

- Detracts aesthetically

- Generates too little energy for such a high construction cost

- Opaque rear sides of panels and supporting scaffolding completely block tenants' view from the south side

- Compromises daylighting on the south side

Hayes was skeptical about the idea from the start, but he listened attentively as team members reported on extensive energy models showing that the south array was critical. Achieving an EUI of 16 would be stretching the limits of building technology to levels never before achieved and it would be a shame to build a superbly efficient building only to fail to achieve net zero energy by producing fewer kilowatt hours from the rooftop arrays than the building used. While meeting the energy needs of the building was the primary driver for the south array, designers felt the distinctive visible statement it would make about the importance of solar energy also supported project goals to heighten awareness about sustainable design.

In the end, Hayes respectfully but decisively vetoed the idea. To his mind, the only "statement" such a super-expensive, marginally productive add-on would make about solar energy was that it is wildly expensive and horribly unattractive. Adding millions of dollars to the budget for 52 kilowatts of capacity would equal an astronomical installed cost per watt. As a prominent feature in a highly visible project, it would support a popular narrative that solar energy was unaffordable and it would become a magnet for conservative detractors and hostile news reporters. Finally, Hayes argued, vertical panels generate most of their power in the winter when the sun is low on the horizon. But in the deepest winter months, Seattle tends to be dark and cloud-covered. Nevertheless, Hayes emphasized that the commitment to net zero energy remained non-negotiable. The team was going to have to find ways to trim energy use even further. The vertical array was off the table.

A rendering indicates how a "mud flap" array would have extended from the roof downward alongside the top four stories on the building's south side.

"When you're cantilevering PV from the side of the building at a non-optimal angle, which is what the combover would have required, it's very expensive energy to harvest as opposed to the rooftop. I think it was pretty clear in everyone's minds from the very beginning that getting owner's approval for the south array was going to be an uphill climb."

SCOTT BEVAN
PAE

"The south array was dismissed for aesthetic reasons (from both inside and outside of the building), and for compromising both daylighting, and view. The ruling factor was that it wouldn't produce that much energy anyway because the sun isn't there; it's not available. That was just a temporary cul de sac that was relatively brief in duration and then we moved along."

STEVEN STRONG
Solar Design Associates

"We had a remarkably collaborative design process. After working an issue long enough, a consensus almost always formed about the best solution. Because Schuchart and Point 32 were involved from the beginning, very few agreed-upon solutions were later undercut by value engineering. Only on rare occasions did I exercise the owner's prerogative to make a command decision, and then only when there was a difference of opinion on the team. The mud flap was one of those times. In retrospect, it was clearly the correct decision. Thank heavens!"

DENIS HAYES
Bullitt Foundation

"Some of us, myself included, became enamored of that south array. It would have been this iconic image; it's what everyone would have seen. Ultimately, it came down to a matter of cost (the armature required to hold it was terribly expensive) and performance. We wouldn't have gotten that much bang for the buck."

ROB PEÑA
Integrated Design Lab

THE BRIGHTEST SOLUTION

Through dozens of iterations exploring various possible configurations, the team settled on the final size, shape, and output of the photovoltaics:

575 PANELS

425 WATTS PER PANEL

14,303 SQUARE FEET OF COLLECTION AREA

DIRECT CURRENT RATING OF 244.38 KW

AVERAGE ANNUAL ENERGY GENERATION OF 240,000 KWH

The Bullitt Center solar panels were manufactured by California-based SunPower Corporation, founded in the 1970s by Richard Swanson, a fellow solar pioneer and longstanding friend of Hayes. At the time they were specified for the Bullitt Center, the SunPower panels were the most efficient commercially available modules aside from such massive industrial applications as the United States space program. Seeking to power a six-story building from the sunlight that falls on its roof, the team need to convert just as much of that sunlight into electricity as it could.

Moreover, the team sought to make the "roof" as large as possible. Instead of having an array that merely covered the building, they wanted to extend it out beyond the building's footprint (in a manner resembling a mortar board worn at graduation ceremonies). Because of simple geometry, such extensions of the roof at the perimeter would yield great increases in square footage. If the solar array could simply stretch over the surrounding sidewalks, the total surface area would increase from 10,000 square feet to ~14,000 square feet.

The sidewalks, though, are the property of the City of Seattle, not of the Bullitt Foundation, and the city therefore also owned the air rights stretching above them. For the Bullitt Center to place a solar array within an airspace owned by the city, it would have to create a legal basis for such a transaction and then rent the airspace from the city. Cloudy Seattle, to no one's surprise, had no legal provisions covering solar arrays. The closest analogy was an ordinance permitting skybridges from one building to another. But the solar array would not carry pedestrian traffic and the high rental fees charged for skybridges would have added a huge annual cost to such an extension. Hayes and his colleagues appealed to the city, persuading them not just to allow the array to extend into public airspace, but 1) to write an allowance into the municipal code that would permit "solar canopies" on other buildings as well, and 2) to keep the leasing cost sufficiently low so it would not deter similar future solar expansion.

This political decision was of pivotal importance to the Bullitt Center, allowing it to produce 34 percent more electricity than it could have if confined to the building's footprint and leading to the distinctive arrowhead shape of the building's roof. Far more than the rejected vertical "mud flap," the solar canopy makes an important statement about the beauty and value of solar technology.

Mapping out the solar canopy was one thing; constructing it was another matter. Once Miller Hull designed the array, it was up to Schuchart, in coordination with Solar Design Associates and Northwest Wind and Solar, to ensure that its tonnage would remain safely and securely in place on the roof. They realized major cost savings by configuring a racking system comprised of off-the-shelf aluminum rails that connect to the PV panels with standard T-bolts. The framework is intended to stay in place throughout the anticipated 250-year life of the building, but it permits the solar panels to be easily swapped out after 35 to 40 years — the expected lifespan of the current generation of SunPower solar modules.

Photo: Nic Lehoux

"We had to figure out how to keep this enormous array up in the air and prevent it from blowing away – and we had to do it cost effectively with Red List-compliant materials. It was a very exciting challenge for us, because it allowed us to leverage our relationships and our desire to be the steward of the Bullitt Foundation's funds all at the same time."

CASEY SCHUCHART
Schuchart

"Everybody on this project leaned forward, including the folks at SunPower. It was an amazing confluence of courage of conviction. Down to the last worker, we all knew we were part of something larger than just a day's work. And it showed, because every goal was exceeded. Denis would not take no for an answer. He engendered enthusiasm and was able to get everybody to a superlative level of achievement. I've never seen a team come together like that in my 40 years in the field."

STEVEN STRONG
Solar Design Associates

99

POINTS OF LIGHT

The pentagonal shape of the Bullitt Center is echoed on its rooftop, creating an irregular field for the PV array. There was no way for four-sided panels to align uniformly across a five-sided footprint. After pondering various approaches, the designers came up with a way to tackle this geometric puzzle that also delivered nested performance and aesthetic solutions.

SKYLIGHTS

It makes sense to place skylights in the top-floor ceiling of any building that prioritizes daylighting, but a solid array would make it impossible to capture light from above. Removing some PV panels and replacing them with skylights boiled down to simple math. A SunPower panel would convert about 20 percent of the photons in sunlight into electricity. A super-efficient LED lamp might convert as much as 18 percent of the electricity back into light. So a PV panel-LED system would convey just 3.6 percent (0.2×0.18) of the sunlight that originally hit the roof into artificial light that illuminates a desk. With skylights, however, 100 percent of the natural light reaches the interior spaces below. As frosting on the cake, skylights are also much less expensive than PV panels plus LEDs.

GAPS

Even with openings for skylights, the PV panels would not line up in an even grid across the roof's geometry. Something along the plane had to give. So the team created a rooftop layout with consistent leading and back edges, then sprinkled openings throughout the remaining three sides with most gaps placed in the sidewalk overhangs. Not only do the holes help break up the weightiness of the looming roof, but they also deliver a delightful result: Dappled light reaches the ground similar to the way sunlight might find its way through a tree canopy.

Photo: The Miller Hull Partnership

"When I first saw the proposed drawing with random gaps in the overhang, I reacted very negatively. The rectangular gaps struck me as having no grace, no symmetry, no rationale. I argued strongly for placing all the gaps over the building itself where they couldn't be seen except from an airplane. But Miller Hull kept pushing back, arguing that the gaps would mimic the dappling effect of light through tree leaves in the park. Candidly, they never convinced me. But I'd recently pulled rank on a number of aesthetic decisions, and I knew I had to yield on some of these judgment calls or risk demoralizing the team. So I gave in. I believed at the time it was a bad decision but not an important one. However, since the building has been up, countless people have commented to me on the beauty of the dappled light, and how the gaps make the solar overhang feel lighter. Miller Hull was absolutely right all along. Thank heavens I was such a pushover."

DENIS HAYES
Bullitt Foundation

101

USING THE EARTH TO MODULATE TEMPERATURE

A ground-source geoexchange system — commonly referred to as geothermal — delivers heating (and occasional cooling on the rare hot Seattle day) to keep the Bullitt Center's interior thermally comfortable throughout the year and keep hot water flowing through its taps and showerheads.

The average office building in Seattle uses three times as much energy for heating and cooling as the Bullitt Center uses for all purposes. By comparison, only 5 percent of the building's electricity is used to power its small, simple heating and cooling system.

The space conditioning system contains four components:

1. THE GROUND-SOURCE HEAT LOOP. Twenty-six five-inch-diameter bores dive 400 feet into the ground beneath the building's west side. A one-inch pipe drops to the bottom of the bore and back to the surface, then on to the mechanical room. That pipe contains a flowing water-glycol mixture that absorbs heat from the earth, which has an ambient temperature of ~53 degrees Fahrenheit (at and beyond approximately four feet below the surface).

2. THE GROUND-SOURCE HEAT PUMP. Five low-energy, water-to-water heat pumps transfer the heat to the building's radiant heating system, heat recovery air handling unit, and domestic hot water storage tank. These heat pumps function in a similar way to the heat pumps that many typical residences have.

3. THE RADIANT COILS. Heated water is then pumped from the heat pump to the radiant piping system in the slab of each floor to provide heating.

4. HEAT RECOVERY AIR HANDLING UNIT. All of the air exhausted from the building's restrooms is drawn to the roof where its energy is recovered by a "heat wheel" and transferred to the incoming outside air. Whenever the windows are closed, the building's entire ventilation needs are provided by one small 100 percent outside air unit with heat recovery.

Photo: Nic Lehoux

In the summer, the entire system can be run in reverse to transfer heat to the cooler earth and return a lower temperature to the inside of the building. In the building's initial year, this was done for less than two weeks. (The principal cooling technologies are cool air flushing through open windows at night and adjusting the exterior shades during the day.) On occasions when cool water is circulated through the floor, the temperature delta between the floor and the air is not enough to cause condensation.

Most commercial geoexchange systems are placed beneath spacious adjacent real estate, such as parking lots, enabling shallower wells to be drilled. But that was not an option at the Bullitt Center. The entire system had to be located within the constrained footprint of the building. At first, PAE expressed concern that there simply would not be enough space for all the necessary parts and pieces. But as the building's energy strategies began to align and overall energy load projections began to shrink, the engineers concluded that instead of taking up twice the site, the geoexchange system required only half of it. The 26 wells' 400-foot plunge begins beneath the Discovery Commons. Situating them on only half of the site allowed the western-side well drilling and the eastern-side basement excavating to occur simultaneously; neither effort slowed or complicated the other.

Photo: Nic Lehoux

"Ever since the Bullitt Center team began to refer to its 'irresistible staircase,' I've gone to other project charrettes and people use the same expression. Because of this building, that phrase is in the lexicon. A thing like that sometimes gets pulled out of the air, but it takes on a life of its own when there's a powerful story behind it. And these stairs really resonate with people."

JASON F. MCLENNAN
International Living
Future Institute

"I remember Denis saying three things from day one. The building had to be net zero energy, it had to be replicable, and it had to have an irresistible stair."

MARGARET SPRUG
The Miller Hull Partnership

"We decided not to condition the stair because we figured if you're going to walk up to the sixth floor you're not going to mind if it's 40 degrees. We just wanted to make sure it was freeze protected. And if it gets a little hot, we open the windows and warm air exits out the top. Not conditioning that space was a big deal energy-wise."

PAUL SCHWER
PAE

104

CONSERVING POWER ONE STEP AT A TIME

From the earliest stage of the planning process, Hayes clarified one thing about the Bullitt Center's main staircase: He insisted it be so compelling that people would always choose their own power over a mechanical lift when physically able to do so. He wanted the stairs to be inviting, tempting, enticing. He said he wanted nothing less than an "irresistible staircase."

Once those words were spoken, the name stuck. Miller Hull sketched many alternative designs for the building's stairwell, always staying true to the goal of irresistibility. They knew that the more beautiful and welcoming the stairs, the less occupants and visitors would push the elevator button.

The staircase is situated on the building's busy Madison Street side and is prominently visible from the exterior. The architects and engineers engaged in lengthy discussions regarding whether or not to condition the space. Heating and cooling the glass-enclosed six-story box could easily draw enough away from the highly protected energy budget to tilt things in the wrong direction, so the decision was made to guard only against freezing. Otherwise, with the help of windows that automatically open and close, temperatures within the irresistible staircase come close to temperatures outdoors.

In the first year of occupancy, people heading to the sixth floor chose the Bullitt Center irresistible staircase over the elevator an average of 70 percent of the time.

For more information on the irresistible staircase and its role in helping the Bullitt Center satisfy Living Building Challenge Imperatives, refer to the chapters on the Health, Materials, Equity, and Beauty Petals.

THE HEALTH PETAL

Built to Thrive

107

The Health Petal: **BUILT TO THRIVE**

Photo: Brent Smith

SUMMARY OF THE LIVING BUILDING CHALLENGE VERSION 2.1 HEALTH PETAL

Petal Intent

The intent of the Health Petal is to focus on the major conditions that must be present to create robust, healthy spaces, rather than to address all of the potential ways that an interior environment could be compromised. Most buildings provide substandard conditions for health and productivity. There is a direct correlation between decreased comfort and increased environmental impacts, since solutions in the physical environment to improve well-being are often energy-intensive and wasteful.

Petal Imperatives

- Civilized Environment
- Healthy Air
- Biophilia

"The Health Petal as it relates to the MEP piece is all about solving problems upstream so that mechanical systems don't need to work so hard, or be as big, or run as often. In the Bullitt Center, we didn't want to have to use brute mechanical force to push and filter air. The building just naturally airs itself out."

PAUL SCHWER
PAE

"We were determined not to let the building have that 'new car smell,' even in its earliest days. The new car smell – used as a selling point by automobile dealers – is actually the smell of poison."

DENIS HAYES
Bullitt Foundation

IMPERATIVE:
HEALTHY AIR

The underlying goal of the Living Building Challenge Healthy Air Imperative is to ensure that interior air begins clean and stays that way, eliminating the need for power-hungry mechanical systems to right airborne wrongs.

One of the best ways to ensure the cleanliness of the air is to ensure that materials brought into the space do not track toxins along with them. Avoiding paints that emit volatile organic compounds (VOCs), for instance, is an obvious solution. (This is another example of the interconnectedness among Living Building Challenge Petals, as the Healthy Air Imperative relies on adherence to the Materials Red List Imperative.)

The Bullitt Center features a ventilation system that allows outside air to flow through all interior spaces regardless of whether the operable windows are open or shut. When windows are open, air enters and circulates before exiting the way it came in. When windows are closed, a dedicated 100 percent outside air system helps to ventilate the interior. Air is not recirculated through any part of the building.

The building's occupants are the most obvious beneficiaries of its clean interior air, but the overall health of the structure also serves others who come in contact with it — maintenance personnel, cleaning crews, and visitors all enjoy a breath of fresh air while in the Bullitt Center.

IMPERATIVE:
CIVILIZED ENVIRONMENT

The Civilized Environment Imperative calls for operable windows that provide access to fresh air and daylight from all interior spaces, specifying the maximum distance between a building's occupants and its exterior windows.

Given the typology of the Bullitt Center, that meant that no worker's desk could be farther than 30 linear feet from an exterior window. But accommodating this requirement in conjunction with the project's ambitious daylighting goals and its tight site constraints proved to be more difficult than anticipated.

Miller Hull factored the 30-foot desk-to-window requirement as they explored different building shapes while PAE simultaneously overlaid daylighting calculations onto proposed designs. At the same time, Point 32 was concerned with layouts of interior office spaces and how they may affect the building's eventual rentability. Adhering to this one Imperative, with its asterisked 30-foot specification, turned into one of the more intense collaborative exercises during the design process.

The building ended up with open floor plans for all individual work areas, each of which is within the mandated distance to windows that can be operated manually (but are programmed to open and close automatically). Conference rooms are pushed toward the core. This layout ensures occupants' proximity to fresh air and natural light while encouraging collaborative — and civilized — work environments.

Photos: Dan Farmer

"After trying design after design with different U shapes, O shapes, T shapes and what felt like half the alphabet, we finally came up with a design that worked so we could meet that damned 30-foot requirement. But it took a room full of smart professionals beating their heads against the wall to get there."

DENIS HAYES
Bullitt Foundation

"The 30-foot requirement definitely had an impact on the design. We found there was a sweet spot where we could get the daylighting we needed and also meet the 30-foot Imperative."

MARGARET SPRUG
The Miller Hull Partnership

"We didn't do anything in this building just for the sake of aesthetics because nature doesn't do things just for the hell of it."

BRIAN COURT, The Miller Hull Partnership

IMPERATIVE:
BIOPHILIA

Miller Hull set out to infuse the building's fundamental structure with biophilic elements — features and forms that nurture the innate human attraction to natural systems and processes — rather than add them later. Not only did this strategy help reduce the Bullitt Center's overall carbon footprint, but it secured its long-term biophilic profile regardless of what tenants might later do to modify the structure.

In their effort to incorporate biophilia, the architects focused on:

ENVIRONMENTAL FEATURES

- Color
- Air
- Sunlight
- Plants
- Natural materials
- Views and vistas

NATURAL SHAPES AND FORMS

- Botanical motifs
- Simulation of natural forms
- Biomimicry

NATURAL PATTERNS AND PROCESSES

- Age, change, and the patina of time
- Central focal point
- Transitional spaces
- Fractals

LIGHT AND SPACE

- Filtered and diffuse light
- Light as shape and form
- Spaciousness

PLACE-BASED RELATIONSHIPS

- Geographic connection to place
- Indigenous materials
- Landscape orientation

EVOLVED HUMAN-NATURE RELATIONSHIPS

- Prospect and refuge
- Exploration and discovery
- Change and metamorphosis

Photo: Brent Smith

Photo: Brent Smith

The building's biophilic elements are intended to mimic nature's tangible and intangible impacts — sometimes both at once. In other words, performance systems solve problems the way nature does (directly, efficiently, and with the least amount of resources) while providing occupants with fresh air, daylight, and rich wood throughout the interior space. Near and distant vistas enhance the connection to the outdoors just as the structure's solidity conveys a sense of safety and refuge.

The Bullitt Center does more than copy Mother Nature's designs; it offers a biophilia laboratory where humans can take what we learn from nature and apply those lessons to ourselves and our relationship with the environment.

"This building is like an animal. Its complex brain and nervous system monitor internal and external conditions then respond automatically. It opens and closes its pores (the windows), it bristles its fur (the window shades), it has intestines, kidneys and a ureter to handle its waste, and its skin was designed to be easily shed like a snake's after it becomes weathered and worn over the course of a few decades."

DENIS HAYES
Bullitt Foundation

TAKING SIX FLIGHTS IN STRIDE

The so-called irresistible staircase, previously mentioned in the context of the Energy Petal, must also be discussed as part of the Bullitt Center's health story. Following Hayes's instructions to create a central stair so compelling it would cut down on the use of an energy-hungry elevator, Miller Hull designed an element powerful enough to connect the building's occupants on physical and social levels.

People are drawn to the stairway, and not just because it can get them where they need to go. As the central passageway among the building's six floors, it pulses with occupants and visitors throughout the day. But with a gentle rise-to-run that allows a more gradual ascent, a generous width that prevents crowding, and a glass enclosure that delivers a visual connection to both the neighborhood and the city — and even Puget Sound in the distance — the staircase also serves as a rather unexpected gathering spot. People often stop to take in the view, make a quick call, or chat with passing office neighbors, all while experiencing a profound sense of place.

On a more measurable fitness basis, the stairs weave exercise into occupants' daily work routines. The vast majority of Bullitt Center tenants choose to take the stairs to move about the building, and even those whose offices are on lower floors often have business to conduct elsewhere in the structure. Data gathered during the first year of operation reveal that people opt for the stairs over the elevator 70 percent of the time. And anecdotal stories about the stairs' impact abound. Hayes has returned to his high school weight (50 years later) since moving into the Bullitt Center, which he attributes to his frequent six-flight journeys combined with his new routine of walking to work on most days.

A HEALTHFUL CLEANING CREW

Keeping a Living Building clean is a complicated job requiring dedication and training.

The third-party janitorial company contracted by Unico Properties had to agree to rigorous "green clean" policies before being granted the Bullitt Center assignment. The cleaning staff must understand the Living Building Challenge and perform their duties in compliance with all of its Imperatives.

In the context of the Health and Materials Petals, only Red List-compliant cleaning products may be used so that the air and surfaces inside the building remain free of toxins. Also, vendors must submit monthly reports to Unico outlining their processes, the products they used, and all employee

training activities. The reporting process is designed to keep vendors accountable not just for the health and safety of the building's occupants, but also for its workers.

"We make sure that anyone we've hired who will step foot in or around the Bullitt Center is performing their work in compliance with the Living Building Challenge. It's our job to make sure they have a depth of understanding and knowledge of what's required."

BRETT PHILLIPS, Unico Properties

115

Photo: Juan A. Hernandez

A NURTURING WORKPLACE

Tenants and their employees get more out of the Bullitt Center than a popular and prestigious office address. The building's human-friendly features makes it an appealing option for organizations interested in providing their staff with intangible benefits that extend beyond the standard perks.

116

Comfort is a natural offshoot of the Bullitt Center's performance systems. And the more comfortable the workspace, the thinking goes, the more happy and productive the workers. The invigorating fresh air, the inspirational natural daylight (both direct and diffused), the rejuvenating staircase treks, and the cozy interior temperatures all contribute to the experience of being inside the Bullitt Center.

PAE chose radiant floor slabs for heating and cooling, which ensures that interior spaces reflect exterior seasonal realities. The radiant energy affects the warmth or coolness of the air and the furnishings in each room in a manner that is more adaptable to the human body than blowing heated or cooled air into the space. Unlike in typical office buildings, where thermostats are programmed to a constant setting throughout the year, occupants of the Bullitt Center can dress for the weather without experiencing a jarring temperature contrast once they enter the structure.

Photo: Brent Smith

117

Photo: Dan Farmer

Photo: Brent Smith

"People sometimes assume that super sustainable buildings require a compromise in terms of comfort; that they're nothing more than weird experiments. That's not true at the Bullitt Center, which is just a better place to be and to work."

BRIAN COURT
The Miller Hull Partnership

Photo: Dan Farmer

THE GREENEST BUILDING

"Being up on the 80th floor of a skyscraper for much of your working life, zipping around on freeways, flying from one time zone to another – we live and work in environments that are extremely different from those in which humans evolved. If we can create buildings that are more strongly rooted in our evolutionary conditions, it may help us get past some of the dysfunctionality of our urban life. To me, that's one of the attractions of the Living Building Challenge."

DENIS HAYES
Bullitt Foundation

A NEW OFFICE NORMAL

Designing to meet the Health Petal Imperatives was an exercise in unlearning bad habits perpetrated for decades by a design-build industry that churned out traditional commercial office buildings.

The Living Building Challenge guided Miller Hull and PAE away from such outmoded features as over-conditioned spaces, harsh artificial lighting, and ubiquitous elevators. Instead, the team let nature take the lead in the Bullitt Center. In so doing, they showed that less can be more in the commercial built environment. Structures with fewer systems and gadgets can be comfortable, durable, affordable, and marketable.

THE
MATERIALS
PETAL

Earthly Goods

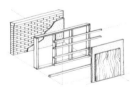

121

The Materials Petal: **EARTHLY GOODS**

Photo: The Miller Hull Partnership

SUMMARY OF THE LIVING BUILDING CHALLENGE VERSION 2.1 MATERIALS PETAL

Petal Intent

The intent of the Materials Petal is to induce a successful materials economy that is non-toxic, transparent, and socially equitable. Throughout their lifecycle, materials are responsible for many adverse environmental issues including illness, squandered embodied energy, pollution, and resource depletion. The Imperatives in this section aim to remove the worst known offending materials and practices. When impacts can be reduced but not eliminated, there is an obligation not only to offset the damaging consequences associated with the construction process, but also to strive for corrections in the industry. At the present time it is impossible to gauge the true environmental impact and toxicity of the built environment due to a lack of product-level information.

Petal Imperatives

• Red List
• Embodied Carbon Footprint
• Responsible Industry
• Appropriate Sourcing
• Conservation and Reuse

"The most Red List-friendly approach is, 'Don't put it in.' It puts you ahead of the game from a consumption and carbon footprint perspective and it lets the same material serve both structural and beauty purposes."

CHRISTIAN LAROCCO
Schuchart

"The Materials Petal really challenged the Bullitt Center team to break new ground in sourcing Red List-compliant and local materials for a building of this scale. The change that happened in the building product industry as a result of the team's dedication and intense work was far-reaching and transformational."

AMANDA STURGEON
International Living Future Institute

AVOIDING THE RED ZONE

The Red List — a compilation of fourteen categories of materials that the International Living Future Institute prohibits in any Living Building — is commonly considered the most difficult Living Building Challenge Imperative to achieve.

Its fundamental purpose is to eliminate known toxins from the built environment. But as more Living Buildings dot the global landscape, the Red List is helping to transform the materials economy by compelling manufacturers to make long-needed changes to the products they provide in the construction marketplace.

Adhering to the Red List takes a significant amount of time and effort, even for modest-sized Living Buildings. At the Bullitt Center, more ambitious than any Living Building project that came before it, the Red List required no less than two years to research, coordinate, and source. Specifying the building to suit the Red List informed virtually every design and engineering decision made along the way. If a product's "ingredient list" included any

forbidden elements, it was rejected and an alternative had to be identified. The process was painstaking, frustrating, and lengthy.

The endeavor might have taken twice as long had the overall goal for the Bullitt Center not been to keep things clean and simple. The plan from the start was to create a building with minimal materials, which complemented Miller Hull's design intent and made the extremely complex Red List vetting task slightly more manageable. Using fewer materials not only meant fewer Red List items to review, but it also means that less of the structure is now hidden behind cosmetic surface layers. Today, the building itself stands proudly as the finished product.

123

Photo: Nic Lehoux

THE RED LIST POLICE

After pondering how best to manage the Red List requirements and calculating that this aspect of the project would occupy at least two people working full time, the Bullitt Center team assigned Red List duties to one person on each side of the construction fence. Point 32's Joe David handled things on behalf of the developer/owner while Schuchart's Morgan Hudson represented the builder. Miller Hull engaged closely with both along the way.

David and Hudson quickly established a division of labor that worked well to manage the monumental task of keeping Red List materials off the site and out of the building. David developed and implemented a protocol for evaluating materials specified by the architects, then interacted with manufacturers to ensure that their products were suitable. Hudson, meanwhile, oversaw the construction zone to educate Schuchart's employees and all subcontractors about the Imperative and to ensure no Red List items crossed the site's threshold.

David and Hudson relied on the following general process:

- Once Miller Hull specified a product or material they wanted to include in the design, they submitted that item to David and Hudson for review.

- David and Hudson studied each item's material safety data sheet (MSDS) — the closest thing the industry has to an ingredient list for building products — and looked for any Red List chemicals that would disqualify the product. In many cases, they had to drill down to sub-chemical aliases or review chemical abstract survey numbers used within larger chemical material groups to determine eligibility.

- Hudson reached out to subcontractors well before construction began to ask for pre-submittals with complete lists of products they intended to use on the project based on Miller Hull's designs. Hudson reviewed those products' data to ensure that the items could be procured and that they met Schuchart's quality installation standards. If both criteria were met, David assessed whether they were Red List-compliant.

124

> "Implementing our material selection protocol meant reaching out to the various manufacturers of the thousands of products that we either considered using or ended up installing in the building."

JOE DAVID
Point 32

> "I earned the nickname 'The Red List Police.' I was doing my normal job of receiving deliveries and inventories and keeping an eye on the crew's daily progress. At the same time, I was hunting down the materials and looking at every product that was new to the site. It opened up a nice communicative relationship with most of the vendors."

MORGAN HUDSON
Schuchart

- If a product's MSDS did not provide sufficient detail to determine its eligibility, David reached out to the manufacturer to request more information. (Because the law requires that only certain chemicals must be identified in the MSDS, up to 80 percent of some products' ingredients can be omitted from their MSDS data to protect manufacturers' proprietary formulas.) He explained to manufacturers that he was part of a team attempting to erect a toxin-free building, and he needed them to reveal their undisclosed ingredients in order to spec their products for the project.

- Manufacturers either responded with more inclusive ingredient lists or denied David's requests. Depending on the contents of the more detailed disclosures, products were approved or rejected for the building.

- When suitable products were identified, David and Hudson returned to Miller Hull with lists of Red List-friendly options for specified items. The architects then modified plans as needed to accommodate any required material substitutions.

> "It generally involved a dialogue with manufacturers. When they said, 'Our ingredient list is proprietary,' I'd say, 'Can you work with me and at least tell me what's NOT in your product?' Usually, they got back to me with a list or a letter saying their products were Red List-free. But if we determined that they contained even small amounts of phthalates or other forbidden materials, I had to say, 'I appreciate your effort but we just can't use it.' This happened with hundreds of manufacturers."

JOE DAVID
Point 32

> "Joe and Morgan never slept."

CHRISTIAN LAROCCO
Schuchart

> "Joe and Morgan were the 'drug dogs' of this project. They'd sniff around the site looking for things that hadn't been vetted. Sometimes, a subcontractor would bring something onto the site assuming it was fine, since it always had been on every other project, and Joe and Morgan would have to say, 'You can't use that here.'"

CASEY SCHUCHART
Schuchart

> "Another key role for me was keeping my own company within Living Building Challenge guidelines. Superintendents who had been out there for 20, 30, 40 years – they're used to materials that are tried and true and they don't want to change anything. Here comes this young woman who says, 'No, you've gotta take that PVC off-site. I don't care if it makes you mad. I don't know yet what the alternative will be, but we're gonna figure it out.' It definitely let me use some of my personality out there."

MORGAN HUDSON
Schuchart

125

PUTTING PRODUCTS TO THE TEST

Beginning in early 2011 and continuing through the completion of the final tenant improvements in 2015, David and Hudson evaluated and logged approximately 1400 products and components as part of their Red List research. Of those, nearly 900 products found their way into the Bullitt Center.

Some illustrative examples of materials that required disproportionate amounts of time and research:

DRYWALL. The project's drywalling subcontractor identified the boards and studs it proposed using very early on in the process, per Hudson's request, making this item one of the first to be assessed for its Red List compatibility. However, the complexity of the drywall and its component parts turned what was expected to be a simple review into one of the most drawn-out of the entire project. David and Hudson had to identify the source of the gypsum and ensure that the drywall studs were not coated with cadmium — as most locally-made studs were.

Photo: John Stamets

"We've been criticized for giving the building a 'raw metal' look. But when you start adding pigments to finishes, that's where the toxins are. The cladding we used is the resolution of which products could pass the Red List test, the durability test, and the maintenance test. Plus, it supports our design philosophy of using honest expression."

MARGARET SPRUG
The Miller Hull Partnership

"The siding is probably the least expensive thing we did, but the reflectivity of the silver gives the building a fantastic quality that is more dynamic than if we'd selected paint."

STEVE DOUB
The Miller Hull Partnership

126

Identifying Living Building Challenge-compliant building enclosure system solutions required sourcing drywall and sheathing materials from Canada to meet appropriate distance requirements, and leaving cladding unpainted to avoid color coatings formulated with Red List chemicals.
Photo: John Stamets

"The cladding of a building is enormously important to its aesthetics and its performance. It is literally like 'Dress for Success' for buildings. An Apple fan ever since Steve Jobs gave me 50 new Macintoshes for Earth Day 1990, I really liked the new Apple Stores and asked whether we could achieve the same look using 100 percent recycled aluminum to keep the embedded carbon ultra-low. Chris Faul, in his quiet, understated way, replied, 'Of course we could – if you had as much money as Steve Jobs. But you don't.' In the end, we found a cladding that has much the same look as Apple, was Red List-compliant, was recycled and recyclable, was produced nearby, and that didn't break the bank."

DENIS HAYES
Bullitt Foundation

CONCRETE CURING COMPOUNDS. David and Hudson vetted many compounds to determine which would be suitable for spraying on the poured concrete to encourage the curing process. Initially, the identified products that met Living Building Challenge requirements did not satisfy basic American Society for Testing and Materials (ASTM) standards, and those that met industry quality standards were not Red List-compliant. It proved very difficult to find a non-toxic product that met the project's specific performance demands. Finally, they identified a suitable product (The Cure WC-E, manufactured by Sinak) that was acceptable from technical and toxicity standpoints.

CLADDING. The Red List heavily influenced the architects' choice for the building's exterior, which emerged after many months of discussing and evaluating different options. Miller Hull sought an alternative to the reclaimed wood siding commonly seen on previously constructed Living Buildings, primarily because it would not meet the project's durability goals calling for a low-maintenance 30-year façade. They considered aluminum for the siding, but decided against it based on cost concerns. Instead, they chose an unpainted steel coil stock siding. Its zinc aluminum galvanic finish would normally be prohibited by the Red List, but the team worked closely with David, Hudson, and the International Living Future Institute to authorize the approach because the finish is on the exterior only and is encapsulated in clearcoat.

127

A newly formulated phthalate-free version of Prosoco Cat 5 air and weather barrier, which protects the Bullitt Center from the elements, illustrates the kind of industry change that can emerge from collaboration between Living Building Challenge teams and manufacturers.
Photo: John Stamets

BREAKING BARRIERS

In a high-performance building located in Seattle, keeping out the rain and wind is imperative. The Bullitt Center team had to identify a weather barrier that would effectively prevent air and water from moving through the building envelope, compromising the tightly controlled energy systems and introducing the risk of mold or rot.

However, the roll-on membrane typically specified by Miller Hull and preferred by the project's envelope consultant — Cat 5®, developed by Building Envelope Innovations (BEI) and manufactured by Prosoco — was suspected of containing phthalates, a chemical compound found on the Red List.

Instead of searching for other manufacturers' alternatives, the Bullitt Center team chose to investigate Cat 5's Red List eligibility more closely, as it was considered the highest quality option. Since the product's MSDS listed several chemicals classified as "proprietary," Joe David contacted Prosoco directly to inquire about Cat 5's non-specified ingredients, but was told the product's chemical formulation was a trade secret. If the company revealed its detailed ingredient list, the representative

said, it would risk Prosoco's position in the marketplace. David pushed back. This was the product they wanted to use, but it needed to be qualified as Red List-friendly. The problem: Despite white papers claiming otherwise, phthalates are known to cause endocrine disruption, which places them squarely on the Living Building Challenge Materials Red List. Even if it is eventually sealed into a building by other materials and poses no threat to tenants, such a product introduces a health risk to factory workers interacting with it during manufacturing and to installers who come in direct contact with it while spraying it on. Phthalates had no place at the Bullitt Center.

After Miller Hull contacted the manufacturer's representative directly to express concerns about the phthalates in Cat 5, BEI

128

and Prosoco requested a team-wide conference call to talk about the issue. During that discussion, they said that their research and development department had previously experimented with different formulations for their weather barrier product line, one of which was a phthalate-free version. They would be willing to explore further to see if it might be a suitable alternative at the Bullitt Center. They needed time to develop it more, they explained, but it might provide the ideal solution. Prosoco requested six months to refine the product, which aligned nicely with the project's construction schedule. Schuchart was just breaking ground on the site at that point (in summer 2011), so the Cat 5 would be needed no later than the following spring.

In early 2012, Prosoco representatives extended an enthusiastic invitation to have Joe David visit their Oregon laboratory to observe a demonstration of their newly formulated phthalate-free Cat 5 product. When he arrived, he saw that it did, indeed, perform as needed, meeting benchmark metrics for air infiltration and water permeability. Prosoco committed to rushing a Bullitt Center-sized order through its Kansas manufacturing facility to have sufficient product on the site if David said the word. He did, and the Red List-approved weather barrier arrived in Seattle three days before it needed to be installed.

Because of the Bullitt Center team's engagement and outreach, Prosoco added a non-toxic alternative to its product line. Soon thereafter, they chose to remove phthalates from every product they sell. Today, they prominently flag their Living Building Challenge-compliant offerings in marketing materials, taking an active role in changing the industry from the supply side.

> *"For the Cat 5 manufacturer, the outcome of all of this
> was that they realized they are the type of company
> that does the right thing. Now, when anyone buys that
> product, it's the reformulated version that didn't exist
> before the Bullitt Center. To have a manufacturer whose
> product is buried in the wall make that change – that's
> the most dramatic example of what can come out of a
> positive dialogue between manufacturer and consumer."*

JOE DAVID
Point 32

> *"Cat 5 is a great air and water barrier and we wanted
> to use it. But it has phthalates, so we rejected it. But
> when they came back to us with a reformulated version,
> we realized we had asked the right question. They
> didn't think there was a market for their non-phthalate
> product but we pursued it and the rest is history."*

RON ROCHON
The Miller Hull Partnership

> *"The Cat 5 story is huge. Because of this building,
> that manufacturer started thinking that its products
> might harm the hormonal systems of the people
> who install it, and perhaps their children. Now,
> they use their 'phthalate-free' formulas as a selling
> point. If endocrine-disrupting chemicals emerge
> as the next asbestos, Prosoco could become the
> go-to provider for phthalate-free products."*

DENIS HAYES
Bullitt Foundation

> *"There were so many times in this project when
> we discovered things that were possible and
> better and more environmentally sound, but
> nobody had ever asked the questions before. The
> Cat 5 story is the perfect example of that."*

BRIAN COURT
The Miller Hull Partnership

129

BRINGING EUROPEAN WINDOWS CLOSER TO HOME

The Bullitt Center's impressive window units offer another example of a building component that satisfies multiple Living Building Challenge Imperatives and serves more than one performance area at a time — including the Energy, Health, and Beauty Petals. In the context of the Materials Petal, the Bullitt Center windows story is now the stuff of Living Building Challenge lore.

Miller Hull and PAE explored curtain wall and operable window options that would meet the project's multiple performance requirements, narrowing their search as much as possible to manufacturers located within an acceptable distance from the site. (Given the substantial combined weight of the glass and hardware needed for all six floors' windows, the materials had to be produced within a 500 km radius to satisfy the Appropriate Sourcing Imperative.) The team considered fiberglass window systems, but they would have required building multiple small windows to create the large openings needed to meet the daylighting design. Next, aluminum windows and curtain wall systems were explored, but they could not meet the required thermal performance.

Then a partnership emerged — the kind that the Living Building Challenge was born to facilitate. Goldfinch Brothers, a glazing contractor based in Everett, Washington, connected Miller Hull with Schüco, a German manufacturer. Goldfinch had been working to bring the Schüco curtain wall system to the Seattle market and the Bullitt Center project seemed to be the ideal entrée. The Schüco system met stringent energy code requirements, its aluminum construction helped it meet the need for large daylight openings, and its triple-glazed configuration helped it exceed thermal performance requirements. The architects approached American vendors, asking whether they had comparable products, but none delivered the same combination of engineering, operability, and elegance integrated into the Schüco package.

As a result of the Bullitt Center, Goldfinch became a manufacturing partner of Schüco. Goldfinch representatives traveled to Germany to study Schüco's designs, returning with a licensing agreement to fabricate the proprietary window system less than 30 miles from the Bullitt Center. Using CAD drawings sent electronically from Germany, Goldfinch worked with Seattle-based Northwestern Industries to manufacture and assemble all of the system's components — including the 500-pound windows.

The windows feature two-inch-thick, triple-pane, argon-filled, double low-E glass units. They automatically "pop out" laterally in line with the building's exterior wall when the outside air reaches 62 degrees (adjustable). Because the windows only open when there is a temperature difference between the inside air and the outside air, they offer a passive circulation system. Warm air flows out of the top of the windows while cooler outside air flows in through the bottom — setting up a natural convective current that rapidly replaces all the air in a room without using fans. When closed, the gaskets sit flush against the inner window frames that are glazed into the pressure plate curtain wall system, which virtually eliminates the possibility of air leaks in the building's shell.

> *"Learning that we could use the Schüco system and get these four-feet by ten-feet windows that move straight off the façade of the building without compromising aesthetics with some clunky system and a lot of operables – that was probably the single greatest discovery on the project. And the fact that Goldfinch put us in touch with Schüco is a great example of contractors being out in front to help change the game."*
>
> **BRIAN COURT,** The Miller Hull Partnership

Photo: Nic Lehoux

"These windows required a lot of electrical items on them because they automatically open and shut and they run off building controls. So the glazers had to educate the electricians on how their stuff works, and the electricians had to educate the glazers on electrical stuff. There was a lot of cross-pollination of trades – more than on any other project I've worked on."

CHRISTIAN LAROCCO
Schuchart

"The windows set up a convective current that keeps the air circulating enough through a natural process that means we don't really need to use fans. In a great many offices, you have to have windows open on different sides of the building to create a cross breeze. But here, even without having the central section of the building open, we still get the convection turning over the air on each side of the building."

DENIS HAYES
Bullitt Foundation

"The choice to use the Schüco window system circles back to the idea of nature-inspired design, where new aesthetic potential is achieved by trying something from a performance point of view. The reason those windows are parallel is because they seal better when they close and the seals will last longer because they're compressed evenly every time. The performance metric drove the aesthetic innovation.

BRIAN COURT
The Miller Hull Partnership

"When I tell people about the Bullitt Center, the windows is one of my favorite topics. It's great how we actually used an idea from elsewhere and brought it locally so we're not creating that big carbon footprint."

ROB PEÑA
Integrated Design Lab

131

Photo: Nic Lehoux

132

THE GREENEST BUILDING

"The next step in this whole construction materials industry puzzle is to figure out a standardized, simplified way for manufacturers to publish information about their products and disclose what they're willing and able to so that project teams can make quick decisions about materials selection. It would be a huge time saver."

JOE DAVID
Point 32

UNDENIABLE MARKET SHIFTS

The Bullitt Center's weather proofing and parallel displacement windows are perhaps the two most dramatic examples of products purely reinvented to suit the Living Building Challenge. But one might argue that the project's less noticeable — and far more numerous — product substitutions that occurred on an almost daily basis led to the more profound market transformations and paved the way for future Living Building Challenge teams to specify appropriate materials more easily.

"For me, the story of the Bullitt Center has been told through a series of game changing moments where new audiences and new perspectives have come into play."

JASON F. MCLENNAN
International Living
Future Institute

Throughout the design and construction phases, subtle specification changes were made to accommodate the Materials Petal. Together, those individual modifications added up to a building with a significantly green product list — one that can be replicated by future Living Building Challenge teams.

Common plumbing systems, for example, usually incorporate PVC pipe and numerous metal connectors. The problem: PVC is on the Red List and most metals historically used in plumbing components contain trace amounts of lead, also a Red List no-no. At the Bullitt Center, the design team and the plumbing subcontractor sought to identify Red List-approved alternatives that would achieve the same results. The solution: They substituted ABS and/or HDPE pipes for PVC and opted for lead-free brass wherever metal connections were required.

With every Living Building Challenge project, more products will be added to the database of suitable materials and more manufacturers will step forward with a wider variety of non-toxic products. Designers and builders will enjoy more choice; manufacturers will more freely disclose their ingredient lists. Gradually, the materials economy will shift toward more sustainable solutions.

"There were no subcontractors who were unwilling to cooperate when we started exploring substitutions. We did a good job finding the people who wanted to be on this project; they all knew there were going to be some difficult things to overcome. But nobody on the team ever said it would be impossible."

MORGAN HUDSON
Schuchart

133

Photo: Pixabay

WOOD: A SOLID MATERIAL CHOICE

Timber plays a vital role in the Bullitt Center's materials story.

134

The building sits on a concrete base, which accommodates the overall structure's substantial load and keeps water and earth away from the water cistern and composters situated on the ground floor. Above the floor of the third level, though, all framing is constructed of heavy timber 100 percent certified by the Forest Stewardship Council (FSC), which rates wood according to how responsibly its source forests are managed.

The timber choice was an easy one for Miller Hull to make. The designers briefly considered various alternatives, including predominantly concrete or steel approaches,

but kept returning to wood for multiple reasons: its carbon-negative footprint, its ties to Pacific Northwest indigenous architectural traditions, its local abundance, and its sheer beauty. In addition, since it eliminated the need to use sheet rock in drop-down ceilings, using wood meant using fewer materials.

The Bullitt Center is the first six-story heavy timber office building to be constructed in Seattle since 1927, and traditional column-to-beam connections in heavy timber construction had not been reviewed since. Classified as Type 4 construction, heavy timber structures have been found to hold up well in fires because it takes time for thick structural beams to burn deeply enough to threaten structural integrity. It was up to the Bullitt Center designers to convince the city that detailing of heavy timber — with a mostly concealed steel connector protected by the wood, which created a fire resistive rating equivalent to that of bulky traditional methods — was as safe as it was beautiful.

It all came down to the steel connectors, which had to be resilient enough to hold the building's wooden beams in place in the event of fire. In the end, Miller Hull's design called for the beams to penetrate the connectors, with direct bearing on the columns that stand beneath. This way, the connectors do not need to be fire-treated (which eliminated a Red List headache, as most fireproofing products contain toxic chemicals).

There is an added cost associated with choosing FSC-certified wood. At the Bullitt Center, that premium was approximately 10 percent. While there is no visible or structural advantage to the certified wood, it is guaranteed to have been sourced in a manner that is environmentally sound, socially beneficial, and sustainable for future generations. In other words, the FSC's mission mirrors that of the Bullitt Foundation.

To help keep the wood-related budget in check and create a solution that future Living Building Challenge project teams could replicate, Miller Hull worked closely with Schuchart to identify the most cost-effective answers to the many questions related to timber construction. Together, the architects and builders found ways to balance constructability, cost, and performance while allowing heavy timber to make its own dramatic impression.

135

Photos: John Stamets

SALVAGED ELEMENTS

Recycling is great. But repurposing is better. At the Bullitt Center, salvaged materials were incorporated wherever possible, either into the construction process or the final material list.

Two examples stand out:

CONCRETE FORMWORK. When it came time to place the concrete podium (extending from the foundation through the floor of the third level), Schuchart instructed the concrete subcontractor to search its yard for any gently used plywood forms that would be suitable for the Bullitt Center. When the building's concrete cured and the forms were pulled away, the concrete stood solid and true, just as expected. The only lingering effect of the salvaged formwork is purely cosmetic: A handful of tiny imperfections can be found on the building's interior concrete wall — evidence of the plywood's previous efforts and a powerful testament to the beauty of reuse.

"Salvaged formwork performs just the same as new formwork. You get small blemishes in the concrete that are revealed when you break the forms, but those blemishes help tell the wonderful story of re-using materials."

CASEY SCHUCHART, Schuchart

TREE FENCING. On most construction sites, standing trees are wrapped in protective plastic netting affixed to metal stakes. Since the lightweight mesh material is inexpensive, it is typically purchased new for each project then discarded at the end of construction. It made no sense to the Bullitt Center team, however, to procure new netting and have it shipped from China (where it is usually manufactured), only to toss it in the landfill several months later. Berger Partnership coordinated with Schuchart to pull tree fencing from other nearby job sites and put it back into circulation at the Bullitt Center, where it kept McGilvra Place Park's trees out of harm's way.

"There were so many moments on this project that came down to these minor choices. Someone could ask, 'Does a little thing like tree fencing really matter?' But it really does. If you think about all the tree protection fencing being installed on all the projects across Seattle, you realize how much plastic material is coming from overseas. We just don't need to follow such a consumptive path."

RACHAEL MEYER, Berger Partnership

IMPERATIVE:
APPROPRIATE SOURCING

The Living Building Challenge specifies the distance different categories of materials are allowed to travel to get to a project site.

With very few exceptions, heavier goods must be sourced within 500 kilometers of the site, while ideas (requiring no freight) may come from anywhere on the globe. Products and services that are classified as medium- and low-weight must be sourced from within specified radii extending outward from the project's location.

Schuchart oversaw the Appropriate Sourcing Imperative for the Bullitt Center. Miller Hull specified products, always prioritizing local options, then Schuchart researched whether each item was viable from a budgetary and quality standpoint. If a product passed the first set of tests, its supply chain was mapped to ensure it could be sourced within its designated radius.

This Imperative is intended to do more than minimize the amount of energy and fuel required to deliver goods to a construction site; it is also designed to infuse projects with local materials, local craftsmanship, and local character.

At the Bullitt Center, as with any Living Building Challenge project, there were certain material options whose origins were slightly complicated, which sometimes meant specifying less obvious products. For example, the project's finished wallboard came from a company in Vancouver, BC that was selected over a Seattle-based competitor because the former used gypsum made in British Columbia whereas the latter incorporated gypsum shipped from Mexico. From a carbon footprint standpoint, the BC manufacturer was the more sustainable choice.

"One day, one of the concrete formwork guys pulled me aside and said, 'You know, these nails we're using are made around here, which I'm glad to know because we'll buy those from now on.' When he was first told he needed to use those particular nails, he sort of pushed back; he wanted an explanation as to why. But as time went by, the idea of local sourcing really began to resonate with him. Because of this project, he will now always make sure the money and jobs stay closer to his community."

CHRISTIAN LAROCCO
Schuchart

Manufacturer location for materials and services must adhere to the following restrictions:

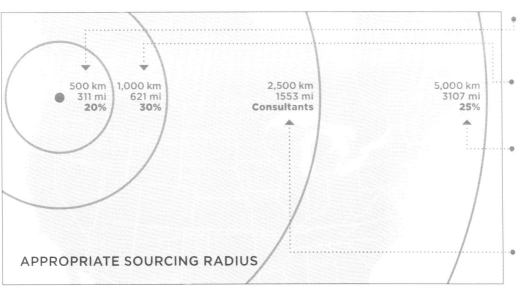

500 km
311 mi
20%

1,000 km
621 mi
30%

2,500 km
1553 mi
Consultants

5,000 km
3107 mi
25%

APPROPRIATE SOURCING RADIUS

- 20% or more of materials construction budget must come from within 500 km of construction site.

- An additional 30% of materials construction budget must come from within 1000 km of the construction site or closer.

- An additional 25% of materials construction budget must come from within 5000 km of the construction site.

  25% of materials may be sourced from any location.

- 100% of consultants must come from within 2500 km of the project location

137

The Materials Petal: EARTHLY GOODS

A CHALLENGE WITHIN THE CHALLENGE

Ask the members of the Bullitt Center team which aspect of the Living Building Challenge was most difficult to accomplish and the majority will identify the Materials Petal. This area of the Standard is intentionally arduous, as it is meant to do nothing less than wholly reinvent the construction material economy.

As more Living Buildings take shape around the world, there will be a longer list of Red List-compliant products, a larger community of manufacturers committed to non-toxic formulations, and a more enthusiastic embrace of sustainable materials practices. In short, project teams will have access to an increasingly robust open-source database of solutions with which to accomplish the Materials Petal. The Bullitt Center, however, was the largest structure ever to accept the Challenge when it registered as an aspirational Living Building, and only the 23rd to receive certification. As such, there was no precedent on which the team could rely for this facet of the project.

There were moments of concern; of befuddlement; of annoyance. But there were very few — if any — moments of pure doubt as to whether the project would accomplish the Materials Petal requirements. The team devoted whatever time and effort was necessary to address each question as it arose, then moved on to the next.In the end, between construction and tenant improvements, the building used approximately 900 non-toxic, responsibly-sourced components that have virtually zero negative impact on human or environmental health.

Photo: Brent Smith

"The Living Building Challenge is really trying to raise the bar with the industry in terms of the materials and products selected for the built environment. It has created a set of constraints that limits what we can buy. The industry that needed to provide us with those materials and products just wasn't there yet, so we had to bring them up to speed. On top of that, we had to engage and educate the subcontractors on requirements they'd never heard of before. The materials task was monumental."

CASEY SCHUCHART
Schuchart

"I was definitely frustrated by the Materials Petal a few times, but I don't think anyone on the team ever thought it was going to be impossible. We kept our construction hats on and continued to work within those parameters. It was all about asking and answering the right questions."

MORGAN HUDSON
Schuchart

"To say that I had nothing but a positive attitude about the Materials Petal for three years would be a lie, but it was the task in front of me. It was stressful and monotonous, but there's kind of a beauty to being able to collect all that information and just follow a tool that you've created to make the best decision possible. In the end, it was a pretty exciting education."

JOE DAVID
Point 32

THE EQUITY PETAL

All Is Fair

141

The Equity Petal: **ALL IS FAIR**

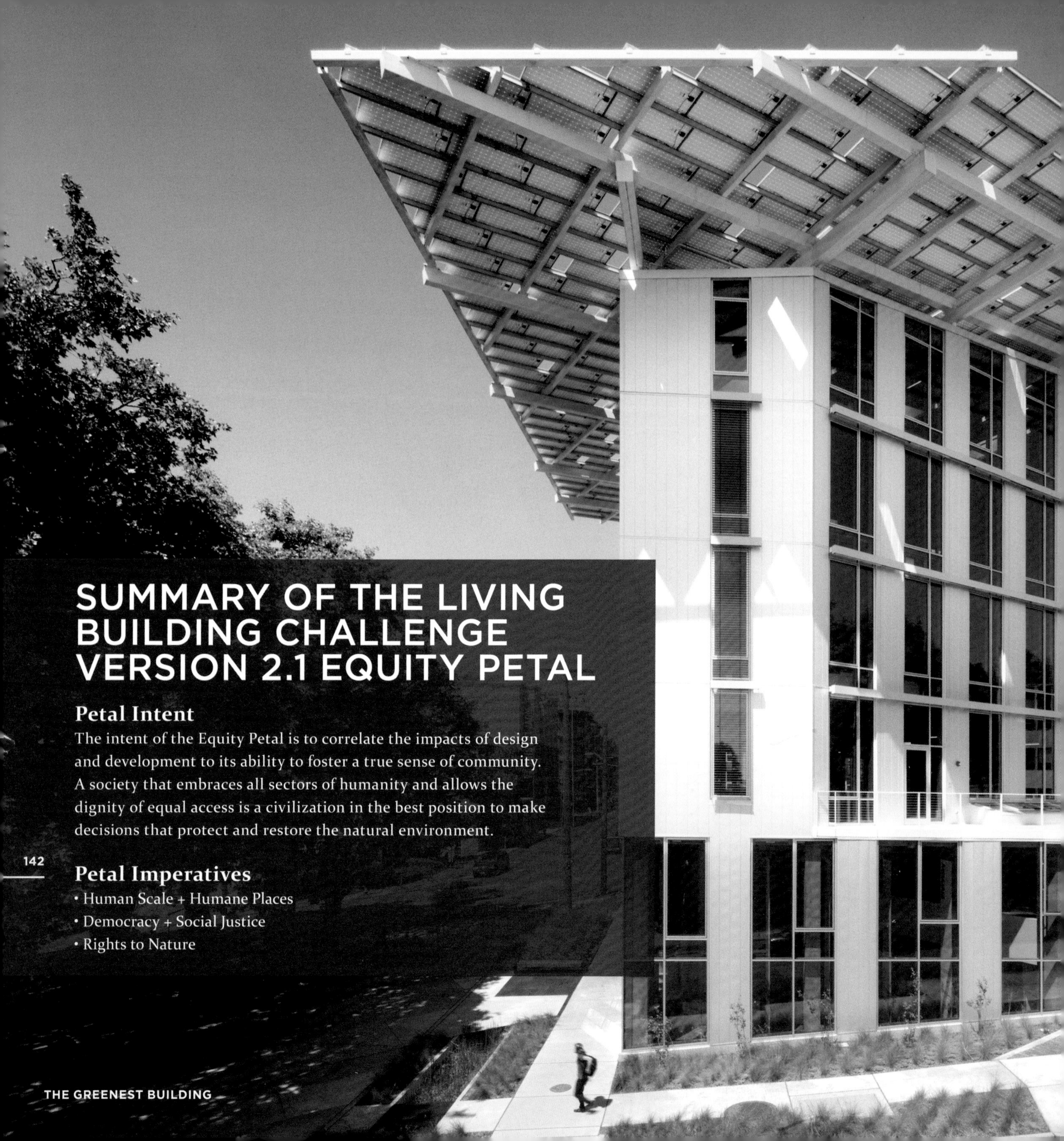

SUMMARY OF THE LIVING BUILDING CHALLENGE VERSION 2.1 EQUITY PETAL

Petal Intent

The intent of the Equity Petal is to correlate the impacts of design and development to its ability to foster a true sense of community. A society that embraces all sectors of humanity and allows the dignity of equal access is a civilization in the best position to make decisions that protect and restore the natural environment.

Petal Imperatives

- Human Scale + Humane Places
- Democracy + Social Justice
- Rights to Nature

Photo: Nic Lehoux

"For most of us, equity is about distributing more resources and providing more opportunities for the poor of this country and the destitute of the world. There are elements of that meaning in the Equity Petal — we established an apprenticeship program for local youth; we created a public park for a neighborhood that has few parks; we offer free wifi to anyone in the park. However, equity, in the Living Building context, is mostly about relationships inside the building. All the offices have open floor plans, with equal access to sunshine, fresh air, views, conference rooms. If your ego requires a closed-off corner office, the Bullitt Center is not for you."

DENIS HAYES
Bullitt Foundation

SHARING THE BOUNTY

The Living Building Challenge Equity Petal aims to create structures that stand as individual micro-societies where everyone who comes in contact with the buildings is treated fairly, equitably, and inclusively.

At the Bullitt Center, applying the principles of the Equity Petal is all about eliminating the types of hierarchies commonly emphasized by traditionally designed office buildings. Its open floorplans and unobstructed sight lines support tenants whose organizational structures are more gently convex than pyramidal, and whose processes are more collaborative than stratified. In the Bullitt Foundation headquarters, for example, there is no corner office, everyone has a view, and no one's desk is positioned behind a door. Every employee has equal access to all the amenities the space has to offer.

Although this Petal focuses largely on issues of equity that affect building inhabitants, it also accommodates global and societal aspects of equity, particularly as they relate to the built environment. During the Bullitt Center's construction phase, Schuchart oversaw an apprenticeship program that gave valuable experience to under-employed workers interested in pursuing careers in one of the trades. The trainees were carefully supervised to ensure that two key goals were met: Apprentices received a level of experience that would prepare them for future employment, and the level of craftsmanship required to ensure the Bullitt Center's eventual designation as a high-performance Class A office building was never compromised.

143

IMPERATIVE:
HUMAN SCALE AND HUMANE PLACES

Even at six stories tall and with a rooftop array that reaches outward well beyond its footprint, the Bullitt Center does not loom over anyone who passes or enters it. It is relatable on an individual human level.

Miller Hull carefully balanced the building's weightier elements with design features that modulate its mass and ensure its approachability.

- Floor-to-ceiling glazing allows an interaction between the building's occupants and passersby, particularly on the ground level.

- The exterior massing steps back from the property line above the second floor, creating a less bulky exterior profile.

- Vertical pressure caps on the curtain wall are vertical fins while the horizontals were left off, which helps to break down the scale of the structure and lends a sense of honesty and transparency about how it is held together.

- Voids in the PV array help break up the solidity of the potentially looming overhead surface, sending dappled light and color to the surrounding ground surfaces and giving pedestrians glimpses of sky.

- Housings for the interior motorized window blinds are set back from the façade so that horizontal shadow lines helps balance the strong vertical rhythm of the exterior.

- The public entry's large scale is modulated by sheltering elements, including a protective alcove and a bench.

- The building's seamless connection with McGilvra Place Park softens the distinctions between the buzz of community activities and the work of Bullitt Center enterprises.

144

Photo: Juan A. Hernandez

"Six floors is about the maximum building height for human connectedness with place. When you look out the window, you see people, not ants. Maintaining a human scale in architecture is something that Jason McLennan has written about and I agree with. I like to think of the Bullitt Center as the ideal representation of what works for humans. At least it works for me. It's like a treehouse."

DENIS HAYES
Bullitt Foundation

"We were constantly looking for opportunities to peel back some of these layers that make a typical office building look too bulky or out of scale or, worse, like a big mirror."

BRIAN COURT
The Miller Hull Partnership

"The fact that the Living Building Challenge asks you to keep everything as local as possible keeps the work closer to home. When it comes to the construction phase of this project, that's the core of the Equity message."

CHRISTIAN LAROCCO
Schuchart

145

Photo: PAE

146

"We didn't choose a slow elevator to discourage people from using it; we chose this model because it's very efficient and because we needed the power it generates when it descends. But if you have to call the elevator down from the sixth floor and you plan to travel to the fourth floor, you will probably get there faster if you just take the stairs."

DENIS HAYES
Bullitt Foundation

IMPERATIVE:
DEMOCRACY AND SOCIAL JUSTICE

Not every office building doubles as a community asset quite like the Bullitt Center. Adhering to the Democracy and Social Justice Imperative meant more than incorporating universal design features that comply with requirements of the Americans with Disabilities Act (ADA). It meant considering the current and potential future needs of everyone who comes in contact with the structure — occupants, visitors, neighbors, cleaning crews, maintenance personnel, and passersby.

The building's only elevator accommodates individuals with mobility issues (and simplifies the journey for anyone carrying a heavy load), although it occupies a less prominent position in the structure's interior to encourage those who can to take the stairs. In addition to being ADA-compliant, the elevator actually generates energy as it descends by converting kinetic energy captured during braking to useable electricity that helps power its ascents. It operates more slowly but saves approximately 60 percent of the electricity used by a standard elevator.

The design team also made sure to protect against externalized costs, ensuring that the Bullitt Center places no environmental or fiscal burden on its neighbors or community. As a self-sufficient structure, it proves that no building — whether in an urban core or a residential neighborhood — needs to tax its surroundings in order to perform well.

Tapping local expertise during construction was a way for the team to adhere to Imperatives of both the Equity and Materials Petals. Schuchart looked first to Seattle-area subcontractors to fill the roster of tradespersons who would put their stamps on the Bullitt Center, keeping the dollars and the bragging rights local.

147

> *"We were very sensitive about sunlight and fresh air, even worrying about how we might affect the building that sits four lanes and two sidewalks away from us across Madison. We could, in theory, cast a shadow low on its southern wall for about two weeks each year, although that would be in December when the Seattle sky is generally a grey blanket of clouds so there are rarely any shadows. Still, we put a lot of thought into things like that."*

DENIS HAYES
Bullitt Foundation

IMPERATIVE:
RIGHTS TO NATURE

Just as occupants share equal access to views and sunlight from inside the Bullitt Center, neighbors also retain their rights to the natural bounty that surrounds the building. The Rights to Nature Imperative prevents a Living Building from blocking any person's or adjacent structure's access to fresh air, sunlight, and natural waterways. If it is to mimic the performance of native vegetation, a Living Building should use only the resources that exist on its own site and never threaten the viability of another in order to survive.

Accomplishing the goals of this Imperative tends to be more difficult in urban settings, where projects can approach (or even reach) the limits of their lot lines, proximity to adjacent structures can result in "party walls," and added height can cast shadows on nearby lots. (It is commonly understood that views come and go in the urban built environment; the Living Building Challenge does not stipulate that a Living Building has to protect its neighbors' sightlines.)

Since the Bullitt Center was larger than any Living Building that came before it, its design team had no precedent to demonstrate how best to meet this Imperative. Additionally, it is the tallest structure ever to stand on the site it occupies, so interacting with owners of the nearby properties became a key component of the planning process. Miller Hull, Hayes, and Point 32 met regularly with their future neighbors, including the owner of the abutting property who had the right of first refusal on the lot when it came up for sale. (Although that individual passed on the opportunity to purchase the site, the Bullitt Center team wanted to establish a harmonious relationship from the outset,

as the bordering building is the only neighbor not separated by a throughway.) The building in question is to the east of the Bullitt Center, so only sits in the project's shadow late in the day on summer afternoons when the sun has begun to dip in the west, temperatures are warm, and shade delivers welcome relief.

The project's downhill-facing southwestern orientation helped accomplish the Imperative, as it alleviated some of the shadowy concerns associated with the oversized rooftop array. Most of the shadows cast by the PVs hit sidewalks and streets, even during summer months when the Seattle sun is highest in the sky.

> *"A tree on the side of Mount Rainier has access to a certain amount of sun and water. Why shouldn't a building live within those same parameters? We're living within the ecosystem budget for our building – at the 50,000 square foot level, and only within the building's footprint. To me, that's what equity is all about."*

PAUL SCHWER, PAE

Photo: Juan A. Hernandez

150

THE GREENEST BUILDING

> *"We looked at the park's history and what that little triangle had meant to the neighborhood over the years. It had essentially been forgotten. We wanted to reactivate it without harming it; to turn it into a place that people could really use."*

JONATHAN MORLEY
Berger Partnership

> *"As occupants of the building we have noticed how our staff thrive here. We think this is a result of the connection between the building and the outdoors through the abundant daylight, natural ventilation, and the adjacent park."*

AMANDA STURGEON
International Living Future Institute

> *"Very few people went to McGilvra. It was like an isolated island; not a great place to be. Now, there's a beautiful pop-up park that benefits the community."*

RON ROCHON
The Miller Hull Partnership

A PARK FOR A FRONT PORCH

Of all the ways that McGilvra Place Park serves the mission of the Bullitt Center and represents the philosophy of the Living Building Challenge, perhaps none is more poetic than how it ties into the Equity Petal. Improving the green space had always been part of the master plan of the Bullitt Center. Pure and simple, the park is a gift from the building to the community, available for anyone to use and enjoy.

Even the improvement process was a democratic one. The Seattle Parks Department asked the public to submit applications and ideas for how to put money from its Opportunity Fund to work on behalf of parks throughout the city that deserved to be rejuvenated. Once community members weighed in, McGilvra Place Park was named among the Fund's recipients (largely because of its sustainability goals). The Seattle Department of Parks and Recreation, the Seattle Department of Transportation, the Seattle Parks Foundation, and the Bullitt Foundation formed a public-private partnership to oversee the redevelopment of the park, putting the Berger Partnership in charge of landscape design.

Today, the park is a tiny oasis in the midst of bustling Capitol Hill. Its 100-year-old London Plane trees stand proudly, now ringed by a non-consumptive landscape dotted with benches made of reclaimed timber. The stretch of 15th Avenue that runs between the park and the Bullitt Center is closed to non-emergency vehicles, which draws pedestrian traffic through the site and into the green space. Passersby stop to take advantage of the free wifi or for a quick game at the ping pong table made of Red List-compliant concrete. What was once little more than a forgotten section of a city block has been reconfigured into a space that equally honors its natural heritage and its human visitors.

THE BEAUTY PETAL

Elegance Expressed

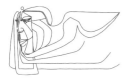

The Beauty Petal: **ELEGANCE EXPRESSED**

SUMMARY OF THE LIVING BUILDING CHALLENGE VERSION 2.1 BEAUTY PETAL

Petal Intent

The intent of the Beauty Petal is to recognize the need for beauty as a precursor to caring enough to preserve, conserve, and serve the greater good. As a society we are often surrounded by ugly and inhumane physical environments. If we do not care for our homes, streets, offices, and neighborhoods then why should we extend care outward to our farms, forests, and fields? When we accept billboards, parking lots, freeways, and strip malls as being aesthetically acceptable, in the same breath we accept clear-cuts, factory farms, and strip mines.

Petal Imperatives

• Beauty + Spirit
• Inspiration + Education

154

Photo: Nic Lehoux

BEAUTIFUL, NATURALLY

It is no mistake that the Living Building Challenge includes such a seemingly subjective issue as beauty among its required performance areas.

Achieving beauty in a Living Building is all about meeting measurable benchmarks within an attractive setting; operating while inspiring; being self-sustaining and outwardly pleasing at the same time. In other words, a Living Building must do what nature does.

There was never any doubt about whether the Bullitt Center would end up as an aesthetically pleasing structure. Miller Hull was selected because of its deep portfolio of striking designs, all steeped in rich local architectural traditions. For this project, though, the firm was asked not just to deliver beauty but to wrap unprecedented performance in a beautiful six-story bow.

The architects' job was to present the building's complicated interconnected systems in a balanced and proportioned form that made regional sense. In short, they sought to mimic the simultaneous efficiency and splendor of the Douglas fir forest that previously stood on the same site. It had to be strong and it had to look natural.

The blend of exposed wood, expansive views, daylit spaces, and functional transparency — all presented on a desirable human scale — draws people toward the building and keeps them comfortable once they arrive. The Bullitt Center is engineered using the commercial built environment's most powerful systems, but designed to stir the human spirit.

155

"When I think about the idea of beauty in nature, it always comes back to a tree. Every part of the tree is there because it has to be there. Our approach to the building was the same: Everything that's there has to be there for the building to perform as a part of an interconnected urban ecosystem."

MARGARET SPRUG
The Miller Hull Partnership

"While beauty is subjective, the outcome is not. People want to see this building; people want to be in this building. To me, that means we've been successful in delivering a beautiful structure."

CASEY SCHUCHART
Schuchart

"The Beauty Petal is highly dependent on context and function. An orchid that is beautifully adapted to the Amazon has a life expectancy of 10 seconds in Siberia. A building that is beautifully attuned to the ecology of the Pacific Slope Rainforest would be wildly out of place in Minneapolis or Phoenix. Real-world buildings have impacts on their tenants, their neighbors, their watersheds, and their energy grids. A Living Building's beauty is rooted in paying attention to its surroundings, its environment, and the needs of its occupants."

DENIS HAYES
Bullitt Foundation

Photo: Dan Farmer

HONEST EXPRESSION

Wherever possible, systems are presented transparently and elegantly to help tell the story of how the building operates. The more observable the systems, the more replicable they will be.

The second-floor green roof is intentionally visible from busy Madison Street, which encourages people to wonder — and even inquire — about what service it performs. Elements of the plumbing and engineering systems are proudly exposed within an aesthetic context to convey their important functions. The basement-level mechanical room is intentionally walled in glass to provide a viewing station for occupants and visitors.

The Bullitt Center's systems are openly expressed with no unnecessary decoration. The building's inherent beauty resides in its stripped-down operational efficiencies, just as with a flower or a tree.

"The architecture of this building is part of the function. Instead of just highlighting mechanical and electrical systems, the design itself is part of the whole system. We've done that to a lesser extent on previous projects, but the Bullitt Center took that idea to a whole new level."

JIM HANFORD
The Miller Hull Partnership

"We kept our systems simple and elegant so we wouldn't interfere with the aesthetics. There's a lot of overlay between the Beauty Petal and simple, minimized mechanical systems."

PAUL SCHWER
PAE

157

EVERGREEN

Wood plays an enormous role at the Bullitt Center — philosophically, structurally, and aesthetically. It lends a uniquely Pacific Northwest character to the design; it offers integrity to the building's frame; it creates an inviting interior environment. (In fact, the exposed timber elements garnered the vast majority — 98 percent — of occupants' votes in a survey assessing which of the building's design features contribute most to its beauty.)

Miller Hull chose not to use wood on the building's façades for cost and performance reasons, but relied on it greatly for the interior. A heavy timber frame sits atop a two-story reinforced concrete foundation. The floor decks above the second floor are constructed using 2"x6" Douglas fir members placed on edge and spiked together. The resulting "car decking" is more than just visually appealing; in combination with the innovative perimeter framing it creates an additional 21 inches of window height, permitting more daylight to enter the building.

Most profoundly, the wood in the Bullitt Center enhances the emotional experience of being in the building. Its beauty draws one in; its warmth makes one feel welcome; its regional flavor makes one feel rooted in place.

"Given the embodied energy and carbon footprint of concrete, timber was a far superior solution from an environmental standpoint. By sequestering carbon in the timber, we have a carbon-negative building."

BRIAN COURT
The Miller Hull Partnership

"During construction when those heavy wooden beams were going up, you couldn't help but be struck by how beautiful it was. Usually when a building goes up, you see nothing but messy concrete and metal work and it doesn't catch your eye. But when the Bullitt Center went up, it was like a gorgeous piece of furniture taking shape."

RACHAEL MEYER
Berger Partnership

"When you look at the stairs' components, they're pretty simple: glulams, plate metal, steel flat bars, pipe rails, and glass. There's nothing particularly special about any of them. What's special is how they're brought together to create such a wonderful environment."

CASEY SCHUCHART
Schuchart

IRRESISTIBLE

The irresistible staircase is discussed elsewhere in this book for its contributions to the Energy, Health, and Equity Petal achievements. But it could be argued that if the stairs had only one rightful place in the larger discussion of the Bullitt Center, it is here in the Beauty Petal.

During daylight hours, the crafted wood and steel-clad steps are bathed in natural light. Broad landings encourage walkers to stop, whether they are headed up or down, to take in the view or simply take in a breath. The stairs' dramatic glass enclosure also enables a relationship between the building and the neighborhood, as it allows passersby visual access to the beauty within.

The staircase is more than irresistible. It could be considered the very soul of the Bullitt Center.

159

The Beauty Petal: ELEGANCE EXPRESSED

AN URBAN OASIS COMES INTO VIEW

McGilvra Place Park stands as the beautiful entrance point to the Bullitt Center. As the designers at Berger Partnership planned for landscaping that required no supplemental water or energy to maintain, they also wove a natural story into the park's layout.

Beginning at the downhill-facing western tip of the park's triangle and continuing uphill toward the broad eastern edge that abuts the Bullitt Center visitor entrance, a very subtle tale is told in wood. Trees are in their wildest form at the base of the triangle, where they stand (or fall) with the least amount of human intervention. As the park widens, wood elements become gradually more sculpted; slightly more polished. Wooden benches are rough cut toward the west, and more architectural toward the east. By the time one reaches the eastern threshold between the park and the building, wood is at its most refined and is directly integrated with the ground-level greywater treatment system.

Wood's story continues inside the building, where timber beams contributing to the very integrity of the structure are visible from the park outside. On this single urban site, wood is expressed in virtually all of its forms — from a fallen log to a powerful means of support within the built environment — each playing off the beauty of the other.

161

The Beauty Petal: ELEGANCE EXPRESSED

Photo: Nic Lehoux

WELCOMING THE PUBLIC

The Discovery Commons is the Bullitt Center's ground-floor visitors' area accessible via the main entrance on 15th Avenue. Open to the public and managed by the UW Center for Integrated Design (IDL), it serves as an open classroom for anyone curious to know more about the Bullitt Center, the Living Building Challenge, or the building's real-time operational performance.

Formal guided tours begin in the Discovery Commons, although detailed interpretive materials spread around the space enable visitors to stroll through the free exhibits at their own pace any time the building is open. The Bullitt Center's official dashboard is wall-mounted in the lobby, displaying up-to-the-minute data on electrical consumption, solar production, rainwater storage, and weather. (The same dashboard is also accessible via the building's website.)

Factoring in guided public tours, events held in the building, and private walk-throughs led by Hayes and other building staff, an average of nearly 150 people visit the building each week for an annual total of approximately 7,500 visitors. Tours are populated by a wide variety of people — from designers and engineers planning their own Living Buildings, to regulators studying the next generation of building systems, to curious laypersons — all eager to learn more about the revolutionary Bullitt Center.

EDUCATING STUDENTS

School groups frequently tour the Bullitt Center, but one collection of students had front-row seats as the building was taking shape.

The Seattle Academy is a private middle and high school spread across five buildings in a three-block radius, all within close proximity of the Bullitt Center. It created the ideal opportunity to introduce the students to the various concepts incorporated into the project. The construction site served as a Living Building laboratory.

Casey Schuchart assumed the role of liaison between the project and the Seattle Academy, leading student groups through the site when new features and systems were going in. In addition, Schuchart oversaw a monthly assembly program that addressed different project-specific subjects at each session. Engaging the students was more than a matter of satisfying their curiosity about the unusual structure being built in their neighborhood; it was about helping them feel connected to the possibilities of the urban built environment.

"The progressive curriculum at the Seattle Academy allows for a lot of creativity, so they were very happy to embrace a project like the Bullitt Center. The students wanted to learn not just about what we were doing, but also about why we were doing it. They were curious about the PV array, the rainwater harvesting, the non-toxic materials – all of it."

CASEY SCHUCHART
Schuchart

Juan A. Hernandez

163

The Beauty Petal: **ELEGANCE EXPRESSED**

"This building has always been a teaching tool. During design and construction, we hosted everyone from heads of state to the head of the EPA. One day Denis even showed up with Amory Lovins from the Rocky Mountain Institute – a genius – who wanted to see the design and proceeded to challenge us on just about every aspect of it. That's something you don't usually have to contend with when you're designing a building."

RON ROCHON
The Miller Hull Partnership

"Denis made it very clear from the outset that he wanted everyone on this project to educate and inspire others; to explain why we were doing what we were doing so it might inspire people to think about the built environment differently."

CASEY SCHUCHART
Schuchart

"A big takeaway from the project for me was the engagement not just with the design and construction world, but with the Seattle neighborhoods – especially members of the community who had all this technical knowledge I guess I didn't expect very many people to have. It was really exciting to be able to connect with people about an idea as big as the Living Building Challenge."

MORGAN HUDSON
Schuchart

ENGAGING THE GLOBAL COMMUNITY

Not surprisingly, the Bullitt Center has garnered a significant amount of attention from every corner of the planet.

Neighbors and municipal officials were not the only ones interested in taking a closer look during construction. There was also a steady stream of visitors from around the world flowing through the site as the building was going up. State and federal elected officials, international heads of state, design visionaries, environmental thought leaders, and other luminaries came to see what all the fuss was about. The project team was collectively responsible for hosting — and educating — them about the building, its systems, and the Challenge it aspired to meet.

165

The Beauty Petal. **ELEGANCE EXPRESSED**

Photo: Nic Lehoux

"In buildings as much as people, real beauty is not just skin deep."

DENIS HAYES
Bullitt Foundation

"I work on a lot of big projects in this town and people are always referring to the Bullitt building – almost like a Holy Grail kind of thing. It's something out there that says, 'We've all got to shoot for whatever piece of this that we can do.'"

MAGGIE WALKER
Former Bullitt
Foundation Board Chair

"One of the major arcs of this project, going as far back as the selection process, was for us to show our willingness to help educate people about this building and the Living Building Challenge."

RON ROCHON
The Miller Hull
Partnership

THE GREENEST BUILDING

"Joe and Morgan led the effort of putting all that we learned about materials into a format that anyone can understand, which means that the processes we used on the Bullitt Center can be duplicated anywhere even if different materials are used. They weren't just doing that for us; they were doing it for the world."

CHRISTIAN LAROCCO
Schuchart

PRIDE OF OWNERSHIP

The architects, engineers, and builders named to the Bullitt Center team — along with every individual contracted to support them — knew from the start that the job of educating others would be integrated into their responsibilities.

The Living Building Challenge requires project stories to be documented and shared as a way of making systems replicable, and Bullitt Center representatives have complied enthusiastically with this condition. But the collective pride in the building would compel those who created it to gush, regardless of whether a standard stipulated they do so.

One day during construction, a member of the team poignantly demonstrated the value of the Living Building Challenge education component. Hayes had invited a professional acquaintance to visit the job site to observe its most recent progress. When the man arrived to the Pike Street crosswalk, he was met by a traffic flagger contracted by Schuchart. She engaged him in conversation as she waved on the cars and

he waited to cross. Did he know about the project across the street? Was he familiar with the unprecedented strategies that would turn it into the most energy efficient office building in the world? Could he believe that a six-story commercial structure would rely fully on composting toilets? Had he ever heard of the Living Building Challenge? Was he aware that this was going to be the greenest office building in the world?

In the time it took to let a few cars pass, this contracted worker — someone who would never win an award for her contributions to the Bullitt Center — enthusiastically and selflessly shared her knowledge of the project with an anonymous passerby. Her delight, Hayes's visitor later reported, was unmistakable and infectious. It's hard to imagine anything more beautiful than that.

PART IV

Proof

The Bullitt Center Lives

169

THE BULLITT CENTER

EXHBT 1.0

Photo: Juan A. Hernandez

GOVERNOR JAY INSLEE
April 22, 2013

OPEN FOR BUSINESS

Poetically, the Bullitt Center opened its doors on Earth Day — April 22, 2013. It was a grand affair, complete with a formal ribbon cutting, poignant remarks by Denis Hayes, enthusiastic praise from local and state government officials, crowds of attentive reporters, and an around-the-block line of eager visitors waiting their turn for a guided tour.

The building was 80 percent leased at the time of its official opening. The Bullitt Foundation made its home on the northern side of the sixth floor with its sweeping views and proximity to the rooftop solar canopy, while the International Living Future Institute (ILFI) planted roots on the ground floor, establishing a direct connection with the bustle of Madison Street as well as the serenity of McGilvra Place Park. Other original tenants included PAE, Point 32, the UW Integrated Design Lab, Intentional Futures (a technology design and engineering studio), and a collection of co-work stations on the fourth floor available for 12- and 24-month leases by individuals or small groups. In the months that followed, Hammer & Hand (a sustainability-oriented general contractor), Interchange Media Art Productions (a video and television production company that rented a section of the co-work space), and Sonos (a maker of wireless audio products and software) added their names to the roster of companies setting up shop at the Bullitt Center. By May 2015, the building was fully leased.

Every new Bullitt Center tenant must agree to certain occupancy guidelines that are woven into their leases. In addition to typical stipulations included in commercial rental agreements, Bullitt Center tenants have to agree to be energy- and water-conscious and to participate in the building's recycling, waste, and composting programs. (Each tenant's energy and water allotments are calculated based on its proportional square footage relative to the building's overall annualized energy and rainwater harvest.) Tenants also agree not to bring known toxins or combustibles into the building. Lastly, tenants are asked to participate in an annual Earth Day open house, when the general public is invited to tour all non-sensitive areas of the Bullitt Center as a way of demonstrating successful sustainable workplace practices.

171

Photos: Juan A. Hernandez

GETTING CERTIFIED

In early 2015, Point 32's Joe David and project team members from Miller Hull gathered all pertinent data and paperwork that documented the Bullitt Center's adherence to the twenty Imperatives of the Living Building Challenge Version 2.1 and formally submitted the building's application for Living Building certification.

(Although the building had been open since April 2013, twelve months of its performance data were tracked beginning January 1, 2014.) Per the conditions of the Standard, the ILFI brought in an independent team of auditors to review the submission and tour the building to assess its performance.

The auditors' official report, dated March 12, 2015, delivered the validation that project stakeholders and interested observers had been waiting for: The Bullitt Center satisfied every one of the rigorous Imperatives of the world's greenest building standard. On April 1, 2015, the project secured its hard-earned place on the roster of certified Living Buildings. The largest structure ever to aspire to the Challenge, the Bullitt Center was the first office building and the 23rd project in the world to be certified as a Living Building.

The Bullitt Center satisfied each Imperative as follows:

SITE

Imperative 01: LIMITS TO GROWTH

The Bullitt Center was built on a previously developed site that is neither on nor adjacent to any sensitive ecological sites. Native and naturalized species have been used in the on-site landscape, and ongoing restoration is not relevant for this small urban site.

Imperative 02: URBAN AGRICULTURE

The Bullitt Center has a floor area ratio (FAR) of 4.2. The Living Building Challenge does not include any mandatory urban agriculture for projects with a FAR above 3.0.

Imperative 03: HABITAT EXCHANGE

The Bullitt Foundation identified one of its many ongoing conservation projects as suitable to meet the demands of this Imperative. It provided emergency interim funding that helped conserve 1,936 acres of private timberland along the Hoh River, one of the few remaining free-flowing rivers in the United States. This land is now within a conservation corridor of the Western Rivers Conservancy, which meets the requirements of a new compliance path for Living Building Challenge Exception I03-E1 Conservation or Parks Projects.

Imperative 04: CAR FREE LIVING

The Bullitt Center offers no on-site parking for motor vehicles. It also increased the density of the site and the surrounding area by replacing the site's previous structure (a one-story building with an area of 3,317 SF and a FAR of 0.3) with a six-story building with an area of 52,000 SF and a FAR of 4.2.

WATER

Imperative 05: NET ZERO WATER

The Bullitt Center provides, stores, and treats its own water through a rooftop rainwater collection system, basement storage cistern, and a basement treatment and pumping system. Rainwater supplies all of the building's potable and non-potable water needs, including drinking, hand washing, dish washing, showering, toilets, and limited landscape irrigation. Seattle Public Utilities supplies water for the fire protection system.

Imperative 06: ECOLOGICAL WATER FLOW

Rainwater collected on the building's roof membrane is diverted to the cistern in the basement; greywater includes all sinks, showers, dishwashers, and floor drains; controlled interval pumping flushes greywater to a Recirculating Gravel Filtration System (RGFS) on the third floor, which uses evapotranspiration and microbial processes to filter the water to permitted standards; cleaned effluent is discharged to a drain field in front of the building; wastewater is treated in ten composting units; excess leachate is pumped to stabilizing tanks; stabilized leachate is picked up monthly and treated locally.

ENERGY

Imperative 07: NET ZERO ENERGY

The Bullitt Center's 575-module, 244.38 kW photovoltaic array generates enough energy to allow the building to operate on a net positive basis. During the 12 months of operation that were evaluated for Living Building Challenge certification, the building consumed 152,872 kWh and produced 243,617 kWh — generating 60 percent more than what it used. The monitoring system report shows energy consumption divided further by major end-use function. Tenants' careful attention to plug loads contributed significantly to the building's better-than-expected energy performance during its audit year.

HEALTH

Imperative 08: CIVILIZED ENVIRONMENT

There are operable windows in every occupied space throughout the Bullitt Center. Non-occupied spaces (entries, restrooms, janitor rooms, kitchen, copy rooms, and areas dedicated to building systems and equipment) are exempt.

Imperative 09: HEALTHY AIR

Ventilation strategies ensure high air quality in interior spaces and helped the building meet this Imperative.

Imperative 10: BIOPHILIA

Each of the six established biophilic design elements is represented appropriately in the design of the Bullitt Center.

MATERIALS

Imperative 11: RED LIST
All materials incorporated into the Bullitt Center are either Red List-compliant or meet the requirements of the relevant exceptions.

Imperative 12: CONSTRUCTION CARBON FOOTPRINT
An independent analysis by the University of Washington found that approximately 3,000 metric tons of CO_2 were emitted, directly and indirectly, during the construction of the Bullitt Center. The Foundation purchased 2,374 metric tons of rigorously certified offsets to compensate for these emissions, which complemented the 626 metric tons offset by the surplus electricity generated by the Bullitt Center's solar array over the first ten years of operation.

Imperative 13: RESPONSIBLE INDUSTRY
All wood used on the project is either reclaimed or FSC-certified. In addition, appropriate advocacy letters were sent to the stone, rock, and metal organizations, as well as ASTM International, encouraging development and adoption of third-party certification standards.

Imperative 14: APPROPRIATE SOURCING
All materials used on the project met the appropriate sourcing requirements.

Imperative 15: CONSERVATION AND REUSE
The project met the required rates for recycling of construction debris, infrastructure for ongoing recycling is provided, and the project has developed and is implementing an appropriate material conservation management plan for the design, construction, operation, and end-of-life phase of the building.

EQUITY

Imperative 16: HUMAN SCALE AND HUMANE PLACES
The Bullitt Center was designed to human scale and promotes culture and interaction among people and the community. It also met the relevant design guidelines for signage and proportion.

"The Bullitt Center was the type of design challenge architects dream about. The project is a new prototype – a building with essentially no environmental footprint – and the performance-based design process required to create it has changed the way we think about design moving forward."

BRIAN COURT
The Miller Hull Partnership

Imperative 17: DEMOCRACY AND SOCIAL JUSTICE
The Bullitt Center allows members of the public to benefit from its amenities, including access to natural light and ventilation and good indoor air quality; public disclosure and transparency of the design and process; sharing of materials research; and an interpretive center that is open to the public and provides regular public tours. Since the project is in Transect L5, public seating has been provided.

Imperative 18: RIGHTS TO NATURE
The building does not discharge any noxious emissions, is neither adjacent to nor includes any natural waterways, and does not block sunlight access to adjacent façades or rooftops.

BEAUTY

Imperative 19: BEAUTY AND SPIRIT
The Bullitt Center contains elements and features that provide human delight and celebrate culture, art, spirit, and place. Exposed wood, simplified wood connectors, large windows for views and natural light, the irresistible staircase, wood conference tables, site landscape, and water features — all chosen and incorporated into the design for their functional roles first — also contribute to the aesthetic impact of the building.

Imperative 20: INSPIRATION AND EDUCATION
Educational programming and materials make the Bullitt Center accessible to the public as an educational tool and inspirational case study. Programs and materials include regular tours, online information, on-site signage, a brochure, a case study, and videos.

174

BY THE NUMBERS

52,000	Gross square feet
$32,500,000	Total project cost
$18,500,000	Direct construction cost
$356	Cost/sf
250 years	Designed lifespan for the building
92	Average Energy Use Intensity (EUI) of an existing office building in Seattle
32	EUI of LEED Platinum office building securing all energy credits
16	Bullitt Center designed EUI
12	Bullitt Center EUI when fully tenanted (estimated)
9.4	Bullitt Center actual EUI in year one
26	Number of 400-foot deep geothermal wells
575	Number of solar panels on the roof
244	Kilowatts of installed generating capacity
243,671	Kilowatt hours generated in 2014
152,878	Kilowatt hours used in 2014
362	Toxic chemicals avoided in building materials
56,000 gallons	Capacity of rainwater cistern
98 out of 100	Bullitt Center Walk Score
28	Estimated gallons of water used per square foot per year by an office building in Seattle
1	Bullitt Center gallons of water used per square foot per year

"While this project's $18,500,000 direct construction cost (or $356 per square foot) is a slight premium for a Class A office building, it is actually a lower budget than the majority of the civic, higher education, and corporate headquarter buildings that I work on. That means many, many buildings can follow the lead of the Bullitt Center within their current budget. In addition, the cost of PV has dropped significantly since the Bullitt Center was built, making the renewable energy system even more affordable."

PAUL SCHWER
PAE

175

"The most relevant part of the whole Bullitt Center story is that Denis set out to achieve this big, hairy, audacious goal. I believe he knew how close to the margin he was, but I'm not sure he sat back long enough or allowed himself to contemplate the hundreds of things that could have gone wrong, any one of which could have killed the project. This was clearly a situation where the whole is greater than the sum of its parts."

STEVEN STRONG
Solar Design Associates

"I was with Denis when we got the report on the first year's energy data. We were sitting in a beautiful, comfortable space that had enough energy to meet a modern office's computer needs and yet it was 83 percent more efficient than the building across the street. He got very excited and asked me, 'Why isn't every building built this way?' The short answer, as Denis already knew, is that it's not that easy. The good news is that it just got easier for everyone else."

PAUL SCHWER
PAE

"We made a huge, bold bet that human creativity could overcome dozens of unprecedented challenges. If Living Buildings can be built and operated in Seattle, the cloudiest major city in the contiguous 48 states, then they can and should be built everywhere."

DENIS HAYES
Bullitt Foundation

"Denis Hayes is one of the few people who could make a plan like this work.. Our whole board knew it. This has all been in the fertile crevice in the corner of his mind for many years. We knew that someday he was going to achieve something that would be a showpiece for the country and the world. The Bullitt Center is it."

HARRIET BULLITT

177

LIVING BUILDING PARTNERS

OWNER
Bullitt Foundation

DEVELOPER
Point32

ARCHITECT
The Miller Hull Partnership

GENERAL CONTRACTOR
Schuchart

**MECHANICAL AND
ELECTRICAL ENGINEERS
AND ENERGY MODELERS**
PAE

LIGHTING DESIGNERS
Luma

STRUCTURAL ENGINEERS
DCI Engineers

**BUILDING ENVELOPE
CONSULTANT**
RDH Building Envelope Consultants

**WATER SYSTEM
ENGINEERS**
2020 Engineering

ENERGY CONSULTANT
Solar Design Associates, Inc.

SOLAR INSTALLATION
Northwest Wind and Solar

CIVIL ENGINEERS
Springline Design

LANDSCAPE ARCHITECT
Berger Partnership

LIGHTING CONSULTANTS
Integrated Design Lab | Puget Sound
College of Built Environments, UW

SHORING DESIGN
CT Engineering Inc.

SURVEYOR
Bush, Roed & Hitchings, Inc.

GEOTECHNICAL ENGINEER
Terracon

TENANT IMPROVEMENTS
Foushee

BUILDING MANAGER
Unico

PHOTOGRAPHY ACKNOWLEDGEMENTS

Ecotone Publishing truly appreciates the skill and talent of professional photographers Nic Lehoux, Brett Smith, Dan Farmer, Juan A. Hernandez, and John Stamets whose work adorn these pages. The work of Brett Smith Photography was provided courtesy of Robin Chell Design. In addition, Ecotone gratefully acknowledges the contributions of The Miller Hull Partnership, Bullitt Foundation, PAE, Point 32, the Berger Partnership and Groundwork Strategies who were all instrumental in procuring imagery for *THE GREENEST BUILDING*.

AWARDS AND HONORS

2015

SUSTAINABLE BUILDINGS INDUSTRY COUNCIL
Beyond Green Award - First Place

AIA NATIONAL
Committee on the Environment
(COTE) Top 10 Projects Award

IES
Oregon Illumination Awards of Merit

2014

ARCHITIZER A+ AWARDS
Architecture & Sustainability
Finalist & Special Mention

WOODWORKS U.S. WOOD DESIGN AWARDS
Multi-Story Wood Design

ACEC
National Engineering Excellence Honor Award

ACEC
Oregon Engineering Excellence Project of the Year

"We had to have a bit of humility all the way through this project, because there were so many times when we said to ourselves or to others, 'I don't know.' What we learned was that it's okay not to know, but it's not okay to stop there. We had to figure things out as we went to make sure everything was properly implemented and managed. Ultimately, that's how we helped each other and this project become successful."

CASEY SCHUCHART
Schuchart

2013

WORLD ARCHITECTURE NEWS
Sustainable Building of the Year Award

ARCHITIZER A+ AWARDS
Architecture & Sustainability
Special Mention

METAL ARCHITECTURE MAGAZINE
Sustainable (Metal) Building of the Year

ENGINEERING NEWS-RECORD | NORTHWEST
Best of the Best Project of the Year

NORTH AMERICAN WOOD DESIGN AWARDS
Citation

ENGINEERING NEWS-RECORD | NATIONAL
Best of the Best Green Project of the Year

ENGINEERING NEWS-RECORD | NATIONAL
Editors' Choice Best of the Best
Construction Project of the Year

2012

AIA SEATTLE
What Makes It Green Awards

FOREST STEWARDSHIP COUNCIL
"Design & Build with FSC" Award

SEATTLE BUSINESS MAGAZINE
Washington Green 50
(Bullitt Center called out for special recognition)

2011

ECOSTRUCTURE MAGAZINE
Evergreen Awards, On the Boards Winner

INTERNATIONAL LIVING FUTURE INSTITUTE

The International Living Future Institute is an environmental NGO committed to catalyzing the transformation toward communities that are socially just, culturally rich, and ecologically restorative. The Institute is premised on the belief that providing a compelling vision for the future is a fundamental requirement for reconciling humanity's relationship with the natural world. The Institute operates the Living Building Challenge, the built environment's most rigorous performance standard, and Declare, an ingredients label for building materials. It houses the Cascadia Green Building Council and Ecotone Publishing.

ECOTONE PUBLISHING

Founded by green building experts in 2004, Ecotone Publishing is dedicated to meeting the growing demand for authoritative and accessible books on sustainable design, materials selection and building techniques in North America and beyond. Located in the Cascadia region, Ecotone is well positioned to play an important part in the green design movement. Ecotone searches out and documents inspiring projects, visionary people, and vital trends that are leading the design industry to transformational change toward a healthier planet.

LIVING BUILDING CHALLENGE

The Living Building Challenge is the built environment's most rigorous performance standard. It calls for the creation of building projects at all scales that operate as cleanly, beautifully, and efficiently as nature's architecture. To be certified under the Challenge, projects must meet a series of ambitious performance requirements, including net zero energy, waste and water, over a minimum of 12 months of continuous occupancy.